Before the Fork

Getting Your Mind Right to Succeed on Any Diet

ROBIN SHEA

Foreword by Paula Deen

Published by Raising Family Publishing
188 Cal Batsel Road, Bowling Green, KY 42104

ISBN: 978-0-9786408-2-8

Dedication

This book is dedicated to the guy who pelted me in the face with a snowball in the winter of 1986, and to the moments in life that could have broken me, they broke me open instead.

To my husband, Greg - Without our struggles, I might have never been opened enough to write this book. After 30 years of marriage, I feel as if we have just begun! I love you.

To my children, Colton, Mac, Rylan, and Rowdy - Boys, having you gave my life purpose beyond my wildest dreams. You will always be my greatest joy.

To Madison and precious baby Coly - To see our family grow is the greatest blessing of all. I love you so much!

To my family, Mom, Dad, Melissa, Kyra, Jay, and Bo - Our story is ours alone and my love is unconditional and forever. I am grateful for the roll each of you have played in my life. I love you all very much!

To my best friend, Kelly - Our conversations are the birthplace of so many ideas. Thank you for being uniquely yourself and inspiring me in so many ways.

Finally, to my friend, Sonny Khalil - It is with great pride that I call you a friend. Your faith in me has been unwavering, and my love and respect for you is eternal.

Table of Contents

Foreword from Paula Deen..vii

Note from Robin 9

Zone Quiz...10

Section One

Chapter One - Hungry for More...16

Chapter Two - The Day Dinner Died...23

Chapter Three - Resurrection Day 26

Chapter Four - The Plan for the Plate..35

Chapter Five - Time to Get Real...39

Chapter Six - Your Why Story...49

Section Two

Chapter Seven

Pillar One: Happiness - Finding Joy in the Journey 63

Chapter Eight

Pillar Two: Discovery Through Journaling..73

Chapter Nine

Pillar Three: Nutrition - Finding Your Forever Plate 89

Chapter Ten

Pillar Four: Fitness - Setting Healthy Fitness Parameters....................105

Chapter Eleven

Pillar Five: Support 121

Chapter Twelve

Pillar Six: Setting Your Expectations & Custom Goal Setting................127

Section Three

The Four Phases of Transformation 139

The 28-Day Experience 139

Section Four

Tips, Tools, and Techniques

Introduction to Tips, Tools, and Techniques.....................................211

State of Being Practices..212

Mindfulness Tips 217

In-Home Practices..218

Social Environment Practices...220

1*2*3* Magic 222

Identifying Saboteurs 225

Embrace the JOURNEY

and the ADVENTURE Begins

Foreword

I've been fortunate enough to call Robin and Greg Shea friends for years. Robin is gorgeous inside and out, a fantastic mother, a loving wife, an amazing cook, and a good friend. She is a superwoman! It's hard for me to imagine that there was ever a time Robin felt so very deficient in any part of her life. Robin had never shared her insecurities with me until now, in this book. *Before the Fork* is an open, honest, and raw account of her struggles. On the outside Robin was perfect, but inside she was struggling with weight management and feelings of inadequacy.

One day when Robin could no longer maintain the appearance of perfection, she collapsed on her living room floor and prayed for guidance. I can relate to this moment; after 20 years of living with agoraphobia, I awoke at age 40, stuck in my bedroom and dying inside. I looked into the mirror and recalled the serenity prayer: God grant me the serenity to accept the things I cannot change; courage to change the things I can; and wisdom to know the difference. It was my first step back outside and step one in setting up my first business, The Bag Lady.

Robin and I both put our family first and live for making memories in the kitchen and around the table. As my family grows, it's more challenging to 'round everyone up for family supper, but we all make it a priority. When I raised my boys, there weren't as many distractions as there are today. Now between sports, electronics, homework, and the ease of fast food, gathering the family around the table is challenging. Robin shares her road map of how she brought her family of six back to the table. Amazingly, in doing so, she was also able to get her family to eat healthier.

We all face challenges in our lives, but how we overcome and succeed should be shared. In these pages, Robin breaks down how she overcame challenges, and her journey is inspiring. I hope Robin's steps to success inspire you to overcome your obstacles to living life to the fullest.

Paula Deen

Visit BeforetheFork.com to access a free download of helpful tips, tools, and techniques to use on your journey.

A Note from Robin

Chances are, if you've picked up this book, you are most likely are looking to lose weight. I bet you have tried every diet under the sun and have had little to no long-term success with your goals. You may even be feeling defeated, depressed, and hopeless that you will ever get where you want to go on your health and fitness journey. Maybe you even are dealing with obesity, diabetes, or other weight-related conditions. Or maybe you are simply a person who wants to maintain their current shape, but feels uninspired to stay committed to the process. No matter what brought you here, I want you to know that I understand.

Fourteen years ago, I was in the same place you are in now. I was unhappy with my body, not properly nourishing myself, but most importantly, I had yet to discover the powerful connection that has to take place between mind, body, and spirit before even hitting the gym or sitting down at your dinner table.

I've spent over a decade bringing my research together to teach others the methods that have completely changed my health and fitness, and in turn, my entire life, for the better. Before you pick up your fork again, I want to walk you through a new journey—one that will get you ready to succeed on any diet, but most importantly, change your entire life for the better. You'll be going through this book with your own perspective on the process, and that's okay. I am here to show you an entirely new way of living that will shift you into joy, confidence, and greater wellbeing.

If you read this book cover to cover and apply my teachings to your life, wonderful things will start to happen. I am so excited to help elevate you to the next level of your life—one that helps you feel AND look your best.

But first, I want you to take a few minutes and answer the simple quiz below. Save your answers, because we'll explore what your results mean later on in the book. Grab your pen and paper, and let's get started...

Zone Quiz

Consider the following scenarios. Read the questions below and choose one of the four answers that seems most true for you.

1. When facing a new challenge that you have not had success with in the past, you most often:

- (1 point) Use past mistakes as a way to make better future decisions.
- (3 points) Feel hopeless and uninspired to try again.
- (2 points) Quit, refusing to put effort into something I am obviously not equipped to do.
- (4 points) Take it day-by-day, some days trying hard and other days wanting to quit.

2. On a casual trip to the grocery store, you encounter an unexpected traffic delay. The statement that best describes your action is:

- (4 points) I can't really say, too many variables.
- (3 points) I would get mildly irritated and look for an alternate route.
- (2 points) I would honk my horn, get very frustrated, and swear.
- (1 points) I would turn up my radio, or call a friend and use the time to catch-up.

3. If asked how much time you spend each morning planning your day, your answer would be:

- (2 points) I spend my days putting out fires and problem solving, so I don't have time to plan.
- (3 points) My days are all about the same, no need for planning outside of appointments.
- (1 point) My days are filled with scheduled activities that move me closer to my goals.
- (4 points) Some mornings I plan, others I jump into action. It just depends.

4. If asked how much time you spend reflecting on past challenges and victories, your answer would be:

- (1 point) Yes, I enjoy being aware of how far I have come and how much I have to look forward to.
- (3 points) Every now and then, just to remind myself not to repeat the same mistakes.
- (4 points) Only if necessary.
- (2 points) I rarely make time to reflect on anything.

5. If you were told by your doctor you needed to lose weight or he was going to put you on cholesterol medicine, you would:

- (2 points) Tell him to write the prescription knowing I would probably not take the medicine or lose the weight.
- (4 points) Tell him it would depend on how bad I felt.
- (3 points) Resign myself to a life of frustrated dieting knowing I can always take the medicine if I can't lower my cholesterol on my own.
- (1 point) Refuse the prescription, find a diet I could live with, and commit to having my cholesterol checked again in six months.

6. If asked how you feel about your past dieting experiences, your answer would be:

- (3 points) I lose a little weight but always manage to gain the weight back plus a few more pounds.
- (4 points) I have a hard time sticking to any diet long enough for them to work.
- (2 points) I hate diets; they make me cranky.
- (1 point) I do not diet, I just eat healthy.

7. If asked what you do for exercise, your answer would be:

- (1 point) I sweat for at least 20 minutes every day.
- (4 point) I intend to exercise but things always get in the way.
- (2 point) I hate exercise.
- (3 point) I try to exercise but I always seem to get injured.

8. If your trainer asked you to bring in your goals for shaping your body, your goals would look most like which answer:

- (2 points) I want to look just like this (insert picture of famous celebrity with a smoking hot body).

- (1 points) I want to balance out my physique and build core strength.
- (3 points) I don't know what I want to look like, my doctor just told me I need to lose some weight.
- (4 points) I want to get down to *xx* lbs. That's what I weighed in high school/college.

9. When you are angry, you call a friend to do which of the following:

- (2 points) I call a friend who will listen to me rant and validate my anger.
- (4 points) I call a friend who will let me rant: and sometimes it helps, sometimes I end up angry at the friend.
- (1 point) I call a friend who will help me see another perspective and help me solve my problem.
- (3 points) I call a friend who will share similar stories with me so I don't feel alone.

10. When you need emotional support, you most often find it in which of the following places?

- (1 point) I find support by aligning myself with people who have overcome my problem.
- (4 points) I talk to everyone about my problems and not just one group of people.
- (3 points) I don't look for support outside of my immediate family.
- (2 points) I don't look for support because no one understands my problems.

Add up the numbers for your answers to each question and find the Zone you scored in. Remember your Zone for later on in the book.

If you scored 10 points, you are **Green Zone**
If you scored 11-20 points, you are **Yellow Zone**
If you scored 21-30 points, you are **Total Reactive Zone**
If you scored 31-40 points, you are **Red Zone**

Now, you're ready to dive in... Get ready to learn all about my own health and fitness journey and the revelations I learned over the last 14 years in Section One...

SECTION ONE

This is my journey.
My thoughts determine
Who I am, what I have, and what I can do.
The power to decide my life rests inside of
Me through the Holy Spirit
And I boldly claim my right to live with
Grace and glory on my side.
My thoughts will reflect a love for myself
Only equaled by God's love for me.
My mind is alert, my heart is open,
And joy and happiness are my guiding light.
Amen.

- Robin Shea

CHAPTER ONE
Hungry for More

Was there ever a time in my life that I felt like I was enough? For as long as I can remember, I had *dis-ease* with my body. I never once remember looking in a mirror and loving the reflection; whoever was looking back at me was never enough. Never thin enough, curvy enough, or voluptuous enough.

I remember being twelve years old and watching *Charlie's Angels,* and I was just in awe of the angels' beauty, sexuality, and gorgeous bodies. Farrah Fawcett was a goddess to my young eyes, and she set a standard of beauty that would become my self-judging measuring stick. This external measurement of beauty left me ill-equipped to embrace any beauty I possessed. My external focus distorted my beauty and sense of self. I carried these feelings of inadequacy throughout my life, never finding peace.

I began the toxic cycle of excessive dieting when I was about seventeen years old. Very disorganized, uninformed, calorically restrictive diets ruled my life. I was either on a strict diet, or I was eating everything in sight; I was a classic "feast or famine" cycle dieter.

After my first son, Colton, was born, I gained a solid forty-five pounds. But being an experienced famine dieter, I was able to sustain myself on a thousand calories a day until the weight came off. I was miserable, but I was thin! With my second son, Mac, I gained only thirty-five pounds, and after his birth, I discovered an entirely new way to manage my weight: diet pills. It was the Fen-Phen revolution.

Fenfluramine and Phentermine were sweeping the nation as the magic prescription for rapid weight loss and increased energy. The drug combination was an anti-obesity treatment that utilized two appetite suppressants. Fenfluramine was ultimately shown to cause potentially fatal pulmonary hypertension and heart valve problems, which eventually led to its withdrawal. And Phentermine, although seemingly safe for short-term use, is just a form of legal speed (in my opinion). Fen-Phen would remain my constant companion for several years. I lost my weight after having Mac with zero effort.

I popped two pills a day, one in the morning — one at night — and I was a rock star. I had no appetite whatsoever, and I sustained life on nibbles off the boys' plates. Not only was I the thinnest I had ever been, but my energy was off the hook. I sprung out of bed every morning, after sleeping with one eye open all night, my heart beating out of my chest and my mind racing, and I eagerly tackled my day. I was the last to bed, first to rise, planning the following day in my mind as I slept. I was constantly serving the needs of my family while also soothing my ego's need for perfectionism every minute.

It was not uncommon for me to have a toothbrush—on my hands and knees—scrubbing the corners of my linoleum floors. My husband, Greg, made sure to get out of the way while I was cleaning. I would clean myself out of the house with freshly vacuumed floors every day. I likened my guest bedroom to a beautiful hotel room. I felt defined by my body and my home, and they were going to reflect "perfection." Truth was, I was a train wreck about to happen, and my path of perfectionism was about to collide with reality.

As always, God knew exactly how to slow down my train. Mac was only five months old, and to my surprise, I had become pregnant again. My pregnancy with our third son, Rylan, was a divine intervention. The second I realized I was pregnant, the Fen-Phen stopped immediately. I enjoyed a 45-pound pregnancy and gave birth to a beautiful, healthy 9-pound, 6-ounce boy.

By Rylan's six-week check-up, I was already back to my pre-baby weight. Fen-Phen was a miracle combination that made me feel as if I was accomplishing healthy weight loss and was in control of my habits. I was on top of the world — until I began noticing something going on with my body.

Painful canker-type lesions appeared in my mouth that further reduced my desire to eat. Within a few weeks, I noticed lesions in more intimate areas of my body, and I began having major digestive issues. Nothing stayed in my stomach; I would either throw it up immediately after eating, or it would pass through me undigested in bouts of diarrhea. Regardless of how thin I was during this time and how in control of my appetite I felt, my feelings of inadequacy never changed. I still picked myself apart and judged my appearance against some fictitious standard that I had set in my mind.

I immediately made an appointment with my gynecologist (and friend), Dr. Kela Fee. She probed and pried into my life. She asked countless questions about my stress levels, eating habits, medications, and so on. She asked questions ranging far beyond the scope of my health. After our long discussion, she cultured my vaginal lesions, drew blood, and sent me home with a hug and a comforting smile. Within a day, her office received the

Before the Fork

results of my culture and blood work. The office called and requested I come back in immediately.

"Robin, there is something wrong," Kela said. "After looking at the blood work and reviewing the results of your culture, the amount of stress that you are under is having a serious impact on your body. You are malnourished. Your body is eating itself; it has stopped digesting food, and you are on the verge of a total collapse."

I thought, *What does that mean? Do I have to stop taking my special pills that help me be Superwoman? Do I have to return to the struggle I always felt with food?*

I may have been able to ignore her medical diagnosis, but the next words she said jarred me awake: "Robin, your boys are watching you wither away, and they need you."

I may have let myself down, but I would never let my children down. Without even realizing it, I had become very sick. I resigned myself at that moment to a life cursed with a never-ending struggle with my weight and self-image. I was killing myself; my relationship to nutrition was way out of alignment. How would I ever find a way to be healthy?

After leaving Kela's office, I went and stayed at my mom's house for a few days. My grandmother lived with my parents, and she was a registered nurse. She went to work rebuilding my gut health. Within a few days, I regained my strength and began digesting my food. I threw the magic pills in the trash and never, ever touched them again.

Within a few weeks, I had gained ten pounds, and the feelings of inadequacy began surging again. Considering death was my alternative, I settled back into the feast-or-famine cycle I knew so well. Although I stopped the diet pills, I wanted to raise my family with a balanced sense of nutritional respect, but I just didn't know what that looked like. From growing up in the South, I knew good food, but I didn't know healthy nutrition.

———

I was pretty much the textbook definition of normal growing up. I'm 5'6", and the most I ever weighed throughout my high school career was 118 pounds. So the idea that I felt inadequate about my body seemed ridiculous, but the feelings plagued me my entire life. Little did I know this discontentedness was the birthplace of desire for my life's work in health and nutrition.

I was raised during the fast food revolution and the explosion of pre-packaged foods. In the late '70s and early '80s, there was no "good food versus bad food"; it was an entirely new world of food, neither good nor bad. It was just different. Foods wouldn't shift into categories of "good" or "bad" for a few more decades. I grew up in a vibrant home, with two sisters and two brothers. There was lots of laughter, lots of drama, and lots of love. My mother was the perfect picture of a stunning Southern housewife; my daddy was a charismatic, smooth talking oilman that all my girlfriends had a crush on.

In that era, life was moving faster than ever before. Many moms went into the workforce; families were splitting up at an alarming rate, and everyone was just doing the best they could to make sense of all the changes taking place in society. This was a very stressful and overwhelming time for many homemakers; their role was changing, and uncertainty left them feeling inadequate and insecure. Martha Stewart was a champion for these women, providing them with the attitude and framework that being a homemaker and master entertainer was the most fabulous and rewarding profession of them all.

Before Martha Stewart, however, there was Doris Burr, my mom. She was the most brilliant homemaker, home-chef, decorator extraordinaire, and all-around tenacious Southern Belle. My dad was a fierce provider, working long, hard hours to provide for his family. He drove trucks, worked in the oil fields and many other labor-intensive jobs, searching for his niche. I think everyone who knew my dad as a child knew he had a special something, but being raised a fisherman's son doesn't lend itself to an abundance of opportunity.

My dad changed his stars when he was introduced to a man who would become his mentor and help him become established as a salesman for an insurance company. My parents' income skyrocketed as a result of my dad's natural abilities and dedication to his new craft. This good fortune took them out of the small-town country life they had always known and landed them in the big city of Beaumont, Texas. Dad was a mover and a shaker; all of a sudden, country club living, dinner out with clients, and home entertaining were commonplace.

Mom felt a little out of place in this new world. She had a thick country accent that she was determined to tame, and she was committed to being as successful in her chosen craft of homemaking as my dad was in his new position as a million-dollar-club salesman. So she went to work with her signature quiet confidence; she would master this new world and shine at every social engagement. Not only was it important that she educated herself, but it was also essential to her that my sisters and I shared in this knowledge.

I can remember her dressing us up and taking us to lunch at fancy restaurants. Waiters served us crepes, escargot, sherry, and cream-laden

Before the Fork

dishes, fancy desserts, and more. Dining out was such a treat, and it made us feel special. We learned which fork to use first, how sorbet between dishes was meant to cleanse the palate, and to allow our chairs to be pulled out for us so that a gentleman could be a gentleman. And she didn't reserve fine food for restaurants alone. Mom would grill steaks at home and serve them on sizzling platters; or we would create a fondue spread fit for a king, and make Crepes Suzette or rich seafood dishes — and let's not forget the decorating.

Mom's design skills, creative party planning, and strategic placement to maximize the perfect party flow never went unnoticed by me. Although my family's dinner table always resembled stylishly presented restaurant dishes, our pantry was another story. My mom was indeed a chef extraordinaire, but she was still just one woman, caring for five children in a quickly changing world.

The fast food revolution and explosion of pre-packaged foods never penetrated our dinner table, but it *did* consume our pantry. You could always find a variety of smoked meats and oysters, crackers, pates, fixings for cheese balls, and more waiting in the cupboards. In addition to these staples, the pantry overflowed with pop-tarts, sugary cereals, breakfast bars, chips, 2-liter bottles of soda (she bought one for each week, and when they were gone, they were gone), Ho-Ho's, Ding-Dongs, Twinkies, individually packaged pecan pies, pudding, and fruit stuffed pastries that were absolutely delicious! TV dinners were also a staple in our freezer; Swanson and Hungry Man commanded an entire shelf. The list goes on: spinach soufflés, mac and cheese, enchiladas... it was all there!

I do not want to convey a sense of judgment here against any home filled with these pantry staples (especially my home). It was a changing world. and families were enjoying the benefits of ingenuity in the marketplace.

As a society, little did we know how impactful these two cultural shifts would be. The birth of the fast food industry, the collapse of the family dinner hour, and the explosion of the pre-packaged food industry were the result of societal forces never before experienced by modern civilization. The negative impacts are still felt exponentially today. It decimated the health of America (and beyond). I have to feel that, on some level, I sensed this impending collapse of our nation's health.

If you grew up in a home where nutrition was secondary, don't beat yourself up. Your caregivers did the very best they could. Don't lean on the past, but look to the future. You may be from a generationally obese family, or a family with a history of heart disease, diabetes, cancers, etc. *Guess what?* You can redefine how your family comes to know food! You can become the teacher, student and benefactor of a healthier way to live. That's pretty exciting! Just decide to become a beginner again, and this book will walk you through the steps to achieve complete harmony with your food world.

Sobriety and a Shift into Nutrition

The other part of growing up was that Dad struggled with alcohol my entire life. Many people I talk to at public events have a parent or family member who struggled, or still struggles, with alcoholism. He wasn't a casual after-5:00-p.m.-drinker, not my dad. He was a Jack-and-Coke-at-11:00-a.m. drinker. I could mix a drink by the time I was eight. I knew how to field calls, cover-up, and distract like a seasoned pro.

Despite his alcoholism, my dad was the most good-looking, compassionate, charismatic man you would ever meet. He commanded any space he occupied, and you could feel his presence when he stepped into a room. When I was 19, we checked Daddy into rehab for the third time; he was 39 years old. Something magical happened this time in rehab. He woke up to his vulnerabilities and surrendered. At the time of writing this book, he has been sober now for 31 years. Praise God!

From the age of 15 to 20, I drank a lot, too. I wish I would have adopted my mom's temperance and good judgment, but I loved numbing out. One morning after an all-night bender, I woke up on the floor of my apartment and called my dad. I drove home to my parents' house and sat with him.

"Rob," (his nickname for me), "think back to every time you have felt shame. Was alcohol part of the story? Think back to the regrets, the unease, and the embarrassment—did alcohol play a part?"

It was like a light bulb went off, and I finally understood. "Yes," I said. We got up from the couch and drove straight to a local AA meeting. It was August 7, 1987, and I turned 21 on August 30, 1987. I was sober for my 21st birthday—ironic, isn't it?

Since I wasn't out partying, my first year of sobriety gave me more time on my hands. I learned how to go to a movie, out to dinner, and out bowling without alcohol being mandatory. Most importantly, the void in my life that alcohol left was aching to be filled. After eliminating alcohol, I had to face my discontentedness with my body again—but this time, I had resources to help me explore how to nourish myself in healthy ways, instead of numbing out. I was now living in California with my family, which played a large role in my growth.

Our healthy community gave me the confidence to wholeheartedly explore a new way of living that, up to that point in my life, I had only been reading about. My curiosity continued to grow, and as it grew it was filled with answers and even more questions. I found myself being able to access different options, opinions and ideas everywhere I turned my head. With that much access to varying information, you can only imagine the confusion; but I welcomed it. I knew I would eventually find my truth.

I spent my days walking through farmers' markets, pop-up shops, and supermarkets amazed by the freshness and variety of natural foods. Veganism was an entirely new concept to me, but in California, it was everyday life. As I talked to locals, I incorporated suggestions into my nutrition. I ate loads of whole grains, sprouts and crisp veggies straight from the garden, and fresh-picked berries with my breakfast.

My family was having a heyday with my new culture. Mom and Dad dabbled within the idea of new diets, but ultimately they fell in back into their old patterns of eating the same Southern foods I grew up with. I had an uncle and aunt that followed a strict macrobiotic diet, but I was the first in my immediate family to set nutritional parameters. Although I was being mocked at home for being a granola-eating, Birkenstock-wearing health nut, it didn't matter; I had an internal force that made me impervious to criticism. I much preferred identifying as a health nut than as a girl known for drinking too often and too much. Stopping drinking allowed me the time and interest to more fully explore my relationship with food. After a year of sobriety, I found myself feeling pretty confident in my new lifestyle.

One day in the summer of 1988, my dad and uncle walked onto a BMW lot where they were greeted by a smooth talking, newly transplanted Texan named Greg Shea. Greg romanced my dad and uncle, showing them details of the car, working his magic as the master salesman he was. At the end of the demonstration, Greg asked if they were interested in purchasing the car, to which my dad replied, "I don't want the car, but I have a daughter you need to meet." My dad brought Greg home to meet me! It only took two dates before we knew we would be married. After a three-month courtship, we tied the knot in Lake Tahoe.

Three years after we were married, we bought our first home in Riverside, California. With our first child on the way, we felt responsible for being homeowners. To afford our new home, we moved twenty-five miles away from Greg's work place. What that means in California commute times is this: one-and-a-half hours to get to work and one-and-a-half hours home, coupled with twelve-hour workdays. It didn't take us long to realize our quality of life together as a family was more important than a long commute.

Two years after our first little blue-eyed, blonde-haired son, Colton, arrived, we left California and moved to Kentucky. My parents had moved to Kentucky three years earlier. While visiting, Greg and I both felt at home, which made the decision to move an easy one. Within a month of moving into our new Kentucky home, our second son, Mac, was born; quickly followed by boy number three, Rylan, only sixteen short months later. We took a breath and four and a half years later, we welcomed our fourth and final son, Rowdy, to the family.

Greg and I were doing our best to embrace the crazy life of toddler boys. Our marriage had evolved into a partnership defined as the following: Greg's job was to financially provide for the family (and maintain the lawn). My job was to care for the children, pay the bills, clean the house, do all the grocery shopping, cooking, etc. Greg would have stepped up and helped me care for the boys had I asked, but my pride would never allow me to ask. Those boys and my home were 110% my responsibility; it may have been self-imposed, but it was my reality...

A reality that, thanks to my fear-based mindset, became increasingly more difficult for me to live with.

CHAPTER TWO
The Day Dinner Died

I would come to understand that my lifelong struggle with perfectionism was rooted in fear—the fear of never measuring up. Like so many women that I meet in workshops and day-to-day life, my motivation to do most things in life came out of my need to cope with enormous feelings of inadequacy.

People often described me as "driven," and that fed my ego. I had to have perfectly mannered children and a spotless, decorated house. I weighed myself each morning to make sure I was a certain number on the scale and never, ever missed a workout. I studied cookbooks and bought all the latest culinary gadgets so I would have chef-like skills in the kitchen. Picture my nightly routine: after I secured a double stack of baby gates at each opening in the kitchen to trap my boys within my sight, I would have one kiddo perched on my hip, one hanging from a baby gate, and an eye on the oldest as he played on the back porch. All of this happened while creating a healthy culinary masterpiece for a less-than-appreciative crowd, and that included Greg.

I tried experimenting with the latest healthy hotdogs or tofu introduced to the market. I was still learning and reading labels and wanted to be a conscientious shopper. Grocery stores were overwhelmed with new food ideas, and every time I visited, I would easily spend up to two hours browsing the latest healthy products and foods. I was determined to make the healthiest choices I could for my family's dinner table.

More than once, I can recall a collective family revolt when I didn't conform to the norm and just serve them canned Spaghetti-o's with buttered white bread and canned peaches; but I wanted more for my family. I didn't fully understand nutrition and what that looked like in the daily life of my family, but I knew whatever I was doing was being met with a tremendous amount of resistance. I would numb out from time to time and cave into their demands, abandoning everything I felt called to do, but once recharged, I would always loop back around to trying to feed them better. So, this on-again-off-again healthy eating became a cycle, just like the dieting cycle I had created for myself.

I was ashamed to admit that my quest for perfection was all to hide the fact that I was just doing the very best I could to keep my head above water every day. The only truths in my life were this: I still loved my husband as much as the day we married, he was still my person even despite the rocky road we were traveling, and I would walk through fire for my kids in a heartbeat, as most mothers would.

As for the rest of it, I break it down like this: I decorated and cooked as forms of therapy. Decorating relaxed me, and I was pretty good at it, because it was my art. In the kitchen, I felt a sense of connection to myself—and I treasured that. The excessively clean home, the perfectly behaved children, the fit and trim body, all of it was an illusion. I loved being perceived as some "superwoman." But, the reality was, I was only super tired. To get real about it, let me call it what it was: my house was spotless because I spent ninety-nine percent of my time in self-judgment. I would scrub, clean, polish, wash, dust, and do it all over again every day. Heaven forbid anyone stopped in and found me anything less than perfect. It was unthinkable.

My children were well-behaved because I was a hands-on mommy; I valued discipline, but in addition to that, I was also an over-controlling mom, very territorial over my boys. I was not "super" anything...except super burned out! (Raise your hand, if you can relate.) With that burnout, there was a journey to a place of sheer desperation as the façade of perfection began to crumble.

⌒‒‒‒

The next painful, yet necessary, moment of my health and nutrition journey took place one fateful day in the spring of 1996. It's a day that will forever be remembered as "The Day Dinner Died" — the day my desire to raise my children in a home with a healthy, balanced approach to nutrition just collapsed under the pressure of daily life. On that day not only did dinner die, but perfectionism died, too. With one fatal trip to the grocery store, an overflowing buggy of random junk food, three cranky and tired kids, an opened bag of dum-dum suckers and box of powdered donuts, the course of my life changed.

Picture this all-too familiar parenting scene in real time: I'm taking the kids to the grocery store at 8:30 pm on a chilly spring night. Colton is five, Mac is two, and baby Rylan is napping in his car seat carrier. (Rowdy was not yet born.) Bringing all the boys to the grocery store was not uncommon. I tried to avoid it, but it was often unavoidable.

We enter the store, and I'm wandering through the aisles, as most mothers do, trying to remember what to buy off of the top my head. I'm stocking up on survival foods—milk, eggs, peanut butter, bread, etc.—but *not one darn thing to make an actual meal.* By this point in the evening, it has been a long day of wrangling the kids, and our schedule is completely thrown off. My head starts to hurt. I'm tossing in random foods that look appealing because I'm starving. The boys are grabbing bags of cheesy chips, boxes of sugary cereal with cartoon characters, and chocolate bars. (Tip: Never go grocery shopping on an empty stomach!)

I finally get to the checkout with a buggy so heavy I almost can't push it. In fact, a box of chocolate chip cookies slides off the top and crashes to the ground. My feet are aching as the boys antagonize each other beside a rack of gossip magazines. Slowly, I'm unloading each item, realizing that the ratio of artificial foods to anything remotely healthy is 2:1. I've wasted a shopping trip on nothing but junk food. *I can't make a dinner from this,* I think to myself.

A wave of dread washes over me. There are too many bags and no room for the baby carrier in the buggy. At that moment, I know I have to ask the question that mothers everywhere hate.

"Can I have some help out to my car?" The store feels like someone turned the heat up a thousand degrees. I wipe sweat from my upper lip.

"Are you okay, ma'am?" the cashier asks.

"Yes," I say. I feel like my cheeks are on fire from embarrassment. *Does she think I'm a bad mom? Does she think I feed my kids cereal all the time?* Rylan starts to whimper in his baby carrier. He needs a bottle, and the diaper bag is still in the van.

"Someone should be over to help you shortly," she says. Hearing her words shreds my last ounce of dignity. Poof! Confidence and dignity are gone.

Up until this moment, I have always been the mom who never needed to ask for help; in fact, I pride myself on never asking for help, including asking for help from my husband. But as I stand here with Rylan in a full-on wail and Mac and Colton fighting each other over a candy bar they fished out of the buggy, I am desperate. My eyes watch the clock, and I pray to get out of the store as soon as humanly possible.

A minute goes by. No one is coming. By the two-minute mark, Mac is laying at my feet, screaming in frustration. Colton is halfway through eating the candy and has chocolate streaks on his chin. An elderly woman in the checkout line shoots me a dirty look and shakes her head. Another mom whizzes past me—with a smiling daughter and fresh fruits and vegetables in her buggy.

A lump rises in my throat, and I try to swallow my emotion. "Forget it," I say to the cashier, "I can handle it."

I take the baby carrier on my left arm so I can twist my body and push the buggy with my right hip. I have Colton grab the end of the cart, and I have Mac wrap his little arm around my leg so that he won't dart into traffic. Off we go, at a snail's pace. Let me tell you, it is the slowest walk of my entire life.

The rain starts coming down hard in big drops just as we reach the van. The boys are cranky and sleepy-eyed as I buckle them each in before I can even begin to unload the groceries. A bead of moisture drips from my forehead. This time I can't tell if it is sweat on my face or rain. I am so exhausted trying to manage this trip that it feels like a second workout in my day as I'm piling the groceries in the back. My clothes are sticking to my body as I walk around to the kids. I find a lukewarm bottle in the diaper bag and pop it into Rylan's mouth.

"Mommy, can I have another sucker?" Mac asks. Colton still has chocolate all over his face. I don't even bother to wipe it with a napkin. Instead, with complete and utter exhaustion, I open a box of powdered donuts and offer one to each of them. The white dust falls onto their shirts—and all over the seats—but I don't care.

I make it to the driver's seat, start the van, and press play on a movie to keep them distracted. I let out a big sigh, and my head falls back against the headrest. We sit in the dark, and I watch the rainstorm with tears streaming down my face. As Colton and Mac inhale their sugary treats like there's no tomorrow, I sob in the front seat. *I can't do this anymore*, I think to myself. My level of self-judgment had reached its threshold. *I can't pretend to be perfect. I'm done.* I am in a deep and desperate place where I am giving in to the world—but I am also giving up on the façade I've worked to the bone to create during marriage and motherhood.

I am giving up on being the perfect mom and wife.
I am giving up on having a healthy meal whipped up.
I am giving up on nourishing my family.

At this moment, dinner dies. At this time in my life, I can't figure out how to be who I am or who my family needs me to be. So, I quit. Sitting in the front seat of my van that rainy spring night with my boys covered in powdered donut dust, and tears streaming down my face, I know I will never be the same. I spend the next four years unplugging from my health journey. I disconnect in the desperate attempt to find relief. Food broke me, but it would also rebuild me. Soon the biggest transformation of all would happen — right at my family dinner table.

CHAPTER THREE
Resurrection Day

After dinner died, my focus switched to daily survival. If that meant eating fast food three times a day, then so be it. Rowdy, my fourth child, was two years old and was being raised in a car seat as we drove the "big boys" to all their activities. My children knew every menu at every fast food restaurant in town. With all three big boys in sports, we were a family on the go with baby number four in tow.

The family dinner table was abandoned at mealtimes, only to be used as a laundry folding and bill paying station. We ate meals in the car either, on the way to practice or after a game. Sleepovers and birthday parties consumed most every weekend, and the love of my life and I barely recognized the love we once shared so deeply. We always parented very well together, but that is where our nurturing stopped. Then comes the day of the second death — and what I call my Resurrection Day.

It was about 7:30 on a beautiful spring day, and I stood by the front door waving goodbye to my three sweet boys as their school bus pulled away. Meanwhile, my baby boy, Rowdy lay sleeping on a pallet beside my bed. Mornings with children are often chaotic as we bundle them up, gather their schoolwork, and feed them a bite before they leave for school. It is a bittersweet time of life as each school bus ride is a marker of time passing too quickly.

As I waved goodbye to my babies, I was filled with an unfamiliar energy. The estrangement I felt from my husband was unbearable. Greg was desperately unhappy in his work, which tainted his perception of the world around him.

That particular morning, the emotions in our home seemed exceptionally high, and the air was thick with negative energy. It was palpable. The birds had even softened their chirps. They sat quietly on their branches lending what I can only describe as emotional support; it seems as if *they* even knew something was brewing.

As I stood at the front door, Greg stormed past and down the hall behind me. My moment of peaceful waving to my children had passed, and it was back to the reality of my crumbling marriage. It seemed like we lived in a constant state of argument, and we had just had another. My throat was dry, so I poured myself a cup of herbal tea. When I tried to take a sip and swallow, I felt like I would choke. Instead of "I love you," our conversations had turned into snarky comments strategically crafted to cause the other pain. Avoidance allowed us to maintain the status quo. Engagement meant toxic outbursts and verbal fireballs.

I trailed my husband's every footstep down the hall to the back door pecking at him like a hen.

"What's the matter with you? Talk to me," I begged. We were always-seeking to prove our point to each other. This spring morning, in particular, we couldn't let it go. We argued back and forth for several minutes, and then, in classic Greg style, he coolly walked out the back, without even a "See you later" and slammed the heavy wooden door behind him. Shaking with anger, I remained at the window, staring out into the yard. I could feel my fingernails digging into the palms of my hands, and in my ears and throat, I could feel the deep thumping pulsations of my heartbeat. My head was spinning, my body was numb, and my emotions were about to erupt. I put my tea down and gripped the triangular island in our hall by the back door. I had never experienced this much anger, rage, frustration, and hopelessness.

How did we get here? I thought. *What was happening?*

My life played out in front of me like a movie. I was failing at my marriage. I was failing at raising my family in a way that my heart wanted. I was frustrated that I couldn't find a better way of living. I felt like there was a noose around my neck getting tighter and tighter with each breath. Everything was falling apart and I didn't know how to fix it.

I know I'm not alone in that feeling — that desperate ache for relief. I had never experienced that degree of negative emotion; it was the darkest moment of my life. As I stood in the hallway of my home, sunlight streaming through the back door, I collapsed against the island. I was at a crossroads.

Then, like a ragdoll, I collapsed into a heap onto my cold brick floor.

My body convulsed in deep visceral sobs, my hands covering my face, and I finally gasped for breath. Through those sobs, something happened that I could only describe as an out-of-body-experience.

That's when God stepped in.

I could feel God physically untying the noose that was suffocating me. And as the noose was untied, all of those emotions of hate, anger, rage, frustration, and hopelessness were lifted. With my face resting on the cold brick floor, I slowly opened my eyes. My eyes adjusted to the sunshine streaming in through the glass of the back door; the light kept growing brighter and brighter in a beautiful, supernatural way.

A sense of calm washed over me.

At that moment, I realized what a powerful God I served. Everything I had ever experienced in life was necessary. God was purifying my heart; He was tenderly and lovingly replacing all of the dark emotions that had been consuming my heart with love, patience, grace, kindness, and forgiveness. I am confident He was responsible for everything that had taken place in my life: my discontent, my perfectionism, my decision to stop drinking. It was all to show me contrast, which led me to clarity, and clarity led me to identify my purpose. Through alignment, and the release of resistance, I heard the clarity of God's will for my life on that kitchen floor.

He spoke to me in a very human language and gave me a step-by-step guide. It was through that alignment that an undeniable path was laid out for me. God told me exactly what he wanted me to do. My divine purpose was clear, and the message I was to take into the world on his behalf was apparent.

In that resurrection, I had a beautiful sense that everything was going to be okay, as long as I had unwavering faith in God's plan for my life. Through a renewed spirit, a renewed sense of hope, and rededication to my family and marriage, I committed myself to following every one of those instructions. Before I got up from the floor, I lingered in prayer, praising God for my clarity and recognizing my responsibility to answer my calling. *First task: heal my family.*

Then, I got up off the floor and began.

Reclaiming the Family Dinner Table

I immediately walked toward my family's dinner table, and two things still stand out in my mind about that moment. I noticed my calm, happy heart. I had absolutely no feelings of being overwhelmed as I sifted and sorted through a pile of mis-matched socks, stained t-shirts, and outgrown clothes. I bagged and marked items for donation and discarded the things that were not salvageable. I brought the remaining clothes to each boy's bedroom and tucked them away neatly in their drawers.

Next, I looked at a disorganized pile of bills. Rather than having feelings of dread, I had a feeling of gratitude as I threw out old bills and created folders in an attempt to organize our financial life. The second thing I noticed was the wood of my table. The depth and variation in the grain, the texture and smooth surface; it was a magnificent table. It was solid, sturdy, and waiting patiently for me. The table that I had abandoned for four years was now the center of my world and a coveted sanctuary; it was Holy, and it was my privilege to breathe life back into it.

In addition to cleaning house, I made a couple of strategic phone calls that I would have never dreamed about making before my Resurrection Day. I phoned my children's coaches and withdrew the two middle boys, Mac and Rylan, from their sports activities. They were only 5 and 6, and I was physically craving to be with them, not in the car or on a baseball field, but laughing across from them at my family's dinner table. I wasn't just craving Mac and Rylan; I was craving every person I shared my life with. God was making us whole again, and these were the first steps. It was a very cathartic afternoon, but it didn't end with a clean table, neatly folded laundry and a moment of feel good emotion. There was more work to be done.

Next, I pulled out some old cookbooks, looking for kid friendly recipes. I wasn't just looking for healthy recipes; I was looking for old-fashioned, family-friendly, cheesy goodness. I wanted our return to the dinner table to feel like a celebration, not a punishment, and if I dished up a kale salad and tofu patties, my boys would not have celebrated. I was looking to nourish my family emotionally. Nutritionally would come later, but for now emotionally was enough. I chose my menu, wrote out a grocery list, hired a babysitter, and away I went...mom on a mission!

When I returned home from the grocery store, the house was quiet. Rowdy was napping, and the boys were not yet home from school. I paid the babysitter and sent her on her way. Greg and I hadn't communicated since our morning meltdown. I am certain he was at work either seething with hate or indifference toward me. I just loved him...that's all. No hate, no anger, nothing but pure, unconditional love. Although I had made a quantum leap that day, I knew he might take a while longer to come around.

In God's divine wisdom and intervention in my life, he provided me with endless amounts of patience. For the first time in my life I was "loving" as God loves: no judgment, no timetable, no reasons to or not to love, just love; the kind of love you receive from a grandparent or a pet. Pure, non-judgmental, endless, abundant love. Most of all, I finally realized I needed to love myself without judgment. And that meant also loving Greg where he stood. Whether he was loving me back or not, it was okay.

I grabbed some old stationary and found myself to writing him a formal invitation to join us for dinner. It read:

This is where the boys and I will be every night at this time, and we would love to have you join us for dinner.

It wasn't overly mushy because Greg is not an overly mushy guy. He prefers simple and to the point. I started cooking dinner around 4:00, just about the time the boys returned home from school and busted through the front door. I had the table set with a tablecloth, placemats, napkins, and flowers; the boys looked puzzled. I shared with Mac and Rylan that we were going to be taking a break from sports this spring. They responded to this by Mac grabbing his art supplies and beginning his next masterpiece, and Rylan saying, "Okay Mommy, can I have a snack?" Either way, it didn't phase them in the least.

But Colton was a little more passionate about sports. He was almost 10, and a great first baseman. I could see the concern in his eyes. I turned to my oldest child and said, "Don't worry buddy, I know you love baseball. I was only talking to the little guys. They can play in the fall or next year, but for now, you are the only one that will be playing sports." He seemed relieved.

By the time Greg walked through the back door, the boys and I were bringing dinner to the table. His invitation was leaning on the counter right where he places his keys. Through the corner of my eye, I saw him pick it up and read it. I just went about my business, gathering the boys and getting us situated at the table. I instructed the boys to join hands, which was hilarious because they had no idea what they were doing. I asked them to bow their heads, and I led us in a family prayer. All the while, Greg was standing in the kitchen, watching but not uttering a word.

He eventually came to the table with an empty plate and filled it with the dinner I had made. He didn't sit with us, though; he went back into the kitchen and ate standing up. I could sense his discomfort, confusion, and curiosity. I knew how much he loved us; we had just forgotten how to be a family, and he didn't know how to re-engage. So he ate quietly, standing alone in the kitchen, observing his family reconnecting. But I wasn't discouraged. My heart was so full of joy and patience, and it was no problem staying committed to God's instruction.

It would be a full week before Greg joined us at the dinner table. But, in the middle of the second week, Greg not only joined us, but he also led our family in prayer. I will never forget the moment he asked the boys to join hands, he bowed his head, and he rejoiced in our family and gave glory to God. Tears streamed down my face as my husband squeezed my hand. Words were not necessary; words were not big enough to describe the love we were finally allowing into our lives; words were the language of man and what we had experienced as a family was the language of God.

In the hallway of my home that spring morning, God gave me a glimpse into the power of forgiveness. I didn't fully recognize what had happened to my heart; I didn't even realize letting go of my resistance was the gateway to my joy. I knew it was a spiritual awakening that had changed the course of my life, my family's life, and started me on a precious, joyous journey. During the months that followed, my family's dinner table continued to nourish us. Here are a few of the lessons I learned through fellowship with my family at our beautiful, big dinner table:

1. *Boys are not born knowing how to behave during dinner; this is a taught skill.*
2. *Prayer, round-robin style, is the best way to learn what is in your child's heart.*
3. *To be heard, you must first listen.*
4. *The dinner table should be a safe place, where everyone is welcome.*
5. *Kindness starts at home.*
6. *Everyone needs to share in the setup and breakdown of dinner.*
7. *Food feeds your body, but fellowship feeds your soul.*

Through our prayers together as a family, Greg and I were learning little things about our children...things you don't learn by feeding them burgers and fries in the backseat of your car. They would pray for a classmate or a teacher at school who was struggling. Or, we would learn about something weighing on their little hearts. We learned of these things through the intimate time spent in prayer. For little Rowdy, he got to watch his big brothers and learn from their behaviors. It was a beautiful progression of commitment to each other and to our family. I celebrated every single moment and victory that God provided.

Greg and I were whole again, and our family was also whole. Our love was strong, and our commitment was even stronger. A moment of surrender erased years of decay, and my life went from a complete disaster to overflowing with fulfillment. However, there was still plenty of work to be done. God had rekindled my desire to nourish my family healthfully, and I could feel the mounting responsibility to teach my family a better way. This time, I felt completely ready...because I had a plan.

⌒——

Somehow through the divinity of everything I had just experienced, in the beginning I innately knew to just focus on nourishing my family emotionally. The time would come to reclaim all of our health, but too much too soon was a bad idea. So, for the first couple of months, I prepared classic family favorites the old-fashioned way with lots of butter, cheese, and dairy. They had been surviving on fast food for most of their little lives, which meant their taste buds were corroded with chemicals, flavor enhancers, food coloring, and more.

Clean foods, *real food*, would be flavorless, unappealing, and would even taste rancid simply because their ability to taste foods was dulled. My desire to be well-educated on health, food, and fitness never went away. I still had a voracious appetite for knowledge, even during the darkest years, and I continued to feed my mind. I just consumed my knowledge in private, and kept my secret healthy world to myself. I knew from my research that clean and healthy food would be hard for my kids to taste initially, but the time had come to implement Phase Two.

After a few months of our new lifestyle, I was ready to step it up a level. I did this through a series of playful exercises and a simple reward system. One night after dinner, I put my plan into action. After cleaning off the table and doing the dishes, I invited everyone back to the table. I had an amazing dessert prepared, and the boys were all smiles. The kids and Greg sat down, and we served up dessert. While the boys and Greg were eating, I launched my plan.

"Okay boys, here's the deal. Monday through Friday, Mommy is going to cook foods that nourish our bodies. I won't be buying anymore packaged cookies, cakes, soda, or unhealthy snacks ,and we are no longer driving through any fast food restaurants." The boys' eyes almost popped out of their heads, and their mouths gaping open, but before they could begin squawking too loudly, I said, "But every weekend I want us to plan a celebration. Whatever you want. We can make a special dessert, go out to eat, and even drink soda."

I could see them getting excited as they began thinking about their special weekend treat. I empowered them with choice, to distract them from boundaries. They didn't recognize the boundaries and were delighted to be in the driver's seat. *I gave enough to gain a lot.*

"Okay, so what's it going to be this weekend?" I gave them no time to think about the new family rules; I moved straight into the close, and it worked! The boys started rattling off ideas, and I jotted them down. Within a few minutes, we had our weekend menu, and everyone was thrilled. I didn't realize it at the time, but I was laying the framework for what would become the *80/20 Lifestyle.*

CHAPTER FOUR
The Plan for the Plate

During the first six weeks of upgrading my family's nutrition and embracing the most basic idea of the *80/20 Lifestyle*, something wonderful happened: I effortlessly lost twelve pounds. You know what I'm talking about—those annoying extra pounds that you yo-yo for years? *Poof!* Gone. Greg stopped struggling with the laundry list of digestive issues he had battled our entire marriage, and I watched as my children's taste buds came to life. It was so inspiring and kept my passion fueled.

In the weeks and months that followed, I would continue refining my family's dinner table beyond food. I was creating an environment of healthy boundaries, acceptance, routine, and tradition. Because I was so vested in my family's dinner hour, I began researching different strategies that would enhance our communication. I had always been a student of personal development; my earliest reading wasn't a romance novel. Rather, I devoured the writings of Napoleon Hill, Esther Hicks, Earl Nightingale, Claude Bristol, Dale Carnegie, Stephen Covey, Viktor Frankl, Norman Vincent Peale and other pioneers in self-development. Now it was time to call on my years of fascination with self-development.

As I sifted and sorted through my books, I ultimately put my plan together. My plan included a twist on old-fashioned bulk cooking, which I called "Meal Stacking." I went on to write my first cookbook titled, *Meal Stacking*, which was over 50 multi-meal recipes. Each recipe was three meals in one; for example, Pepper-Rubbed Steaks, Sizzling Steak Fajitas, and Camp-Fire Texas Chili. I also created a list of suggestions to enhance your family's dinner table experience. I had so much fun experimenting on my family. I introduced conversation cards, we played games, and prayer and reflection were constant practices. I also realized that dinner was so much more than food. Establishing an environment that nurtured my family was critical to the success of reclaiming my family's dinner hour.

When my son, Rylan, was diagnosed with ADD, I began spending a great deal of time researching behavioral modification techniques to help him learn to be more successful without the use of medication. I think it is important to note that in the midst of all of these life changes, I am still a mother with young children; their needs have always been my driving force. Having only 24 hours in a day, learning to use the time wisely was critical. Meal stacking was the perfect, efficient solution when I had to be in several places at once. Rylan's ADD diagnosis was also the launch pad for my fascination with neuroscience and behavioral science.

I went to work learning everything I could about behavior modification and redirecting ADD without medication. (I am not for or against medication; I just believe that behavior modification must be part of the treatment.) This was the beginning of my love affair with human behavior. Through my research, I came across an underlying theme: nutrition. It seems nutrition plays a large role in helping children — not just ADD children, but all children — stay focused and on-point during school.

Once I made the food/focus connection, I began providing my children school snacks that were brain-based nutrition. Soon after switching him to brain-based learning snacks, I received a note from Rylan's teacher that said the foods were not on the "approved" snack list; however, fruit gummies of any kind were. That is when I realized this was a systemic problem running deep and wide throughout our society. The idea of whole foods not being approved seemed ridiculous to me! It took some time, but I was able to create a snack that the school approved, and that the boys would eat.

I explained to the boys why their snacks were changing, and they were a little resistant at first, but I was firm. They eventually came to love the changes in their school snacks. I was unaware of the magnitude of changes getting ready to take place in our lives, and somehow it seems, this small step was paving the way.

So, the addition of research on family communication and what promotes healthy, open dialogue within a family seemed worth the added effort. If this is an area your family is struggling with, my cookbook, Meal Stacking, highlights every suggestion in detail, along with wonderful recipes to get you started on your way. (Visit my website at BeforetheFork.com to learn more about Meal Stacking and to score some tasty recipes.)

Once I started writing Meal Stacking recipes, I was on fire. Colton was still playing baseball, and I would load up the three little boys, let them play in the dirt, and then pull out my notebook and work on recipes. Through the course of normal conversation that mothers have with one another at the ballpark, I began sharing my miraculous story of healing as well as my recipes. Before I knew it, I was invited to speak to MOPS Groups (Mothers of Preschoolers) all over South Central Kentucky, Indiana, and Tennessee. I wasn't a professional speaker by any stretch of the imagination, but I *was* a passionate maven. All I did was share my story as rudimentary and unpolished as it was, and it moved hearts. I knew these mothers were struggling just as I was struggling, and if my story gave them an ounce of hope that their marriage could be strengthened, and they could stand up to the temptation of raising their children in the fast-food lane, then I felt I was honoring my service to God. Little did I know it was getting ready to grow even larger.

In August 2004, a friend encouraged me to share my story of hope and faith with our local news station, WBKO in Bowling Green, Kentucky. The anchor of the morning program, Whitney Ray, liked my message and invited me on the show to share my story and prepare one of my Meal Stacking recipes. Following my first appearance, the station received a wave of calls and requests for more information. With one appearance on local television, a career was born. I would bring South Central Kentucky a weekly Meal Stacking segment for the next six years.

A year and a half into the segment, of which I was receiving no compensation and was costing my family money, I decided to ask for a sponsor. A local company stepped up and began sponsoring the program. The company owned eighty-four grocery stores, and I received $600 a month in the form of a gift card and $600 in actual compensation. With my expenses now covered, it was enough to keep pushing me along for another three and a half years. There were many times while driving to the station that I would look up to heaven and ask if I was living up to the trust that had been placed in me. I would pray that the message I was delivering would impact someone. I also recognized that I was merely the messenger of hope. It was a wonderful time in my life that kept me tethered to my calling.

During the six years I appeared on WBKO, people would often ask me, "Do you want to be on the *Food Network*?" or "What are you going to do next?" My children were very young when I began my unlikely career at WBKO, and they needed me more than I needed a career. I was tempted to expand, but the idea of taking steps toward a larger audience had to wait until the boys were older. In January 2010, the time had come to end my six-year run on WBKO.

Within a few months, a publicist/friend of mine reached out to me and asked if I would be interested in writing a pilot for PBS. Of course! So, I wrote the pilot for *Southern Fried Fitness* based on the *80/20 Lifestyle* I had been using to nourish my family for the past six years. In August of 2010, the pilot was shot, and the wheels were in motion. The producer and I felt we had a good chance of the pilot being picked up in January 2011, but as fate would have it, PBS and two other cable networks immediately picked up the program. They wanted thirteen episodes by October 2010. We got to work fast—writing episodes, filming, editing, etc, and the first season of *Southern Fried Fitness* aired in October 2010.

I now had an opportunity to share my transformation with the whole country, and it was exciting. I approached it from the perspective of sharing daily survival tools with busy moms because I wanted to help them eliminate the feelings of inadequacy and quell their hunger pains at night. However, not too long into writing the show and telling my story to viewers, I discovered that *my process had a complete system inside of it*...and I had never even realized it! I was sharing two clean and healthy recipes and one indulgent recipe. I also included neuroscience tips that people loved — people were writing in and saying that my approach to healthy eating was helping them transform their lives. Viewers asked lots of questions about the neuroscience tips and recipes. That's when I realized that I needed a dialogue to explain the system that happened to me so organically...

Facebook was quickly becoming "the" place to spread your message. With the launch of my new national television program, I naturally started a Facebook page. It seemed as if overnight I had thousands of followers, all hungry to learn how I was living the *80/20 Lifestyle* and what that meant.

I struggled to explain the events that led up to my transformation. Everything for me was very organic, yet oddly systematic. I struggled primarily with my followers' requests for meal plans and recipes. I understand that, naturally, everyone thinks that food is where transformation begins, but it isn't. Food is only one part of the multi-faceted process of sustainable, long-term change. Anyone can lose weight, but to change your life forever requires more. My mission was never to teach myself or anyone else how to lose weight; my mission was to teach myself and everyone else how to change any aspect of your life in a state of joy and inspiration.

My success wasn't found in food — it was found in an attitude and a system. I quickly realized I needed to put a language to the system that had changed my life so that I could teach it to others. I knew providing recipes was nice, but recipes alone would not provide the foundation for my followers to achieve the long-term, sustainable, forever, change my family experienced. This was when I went to work decoding my years of research.

I would sit for hours recounting the events of my life that empowered me to reclaim my family and my family's health. I spent this time creating a system, a framework, which we had been successfully enjoying for six years. I knew there were three forces at work inside my heart and body; forces that joined hands and made my transformation effortless. I began dissecting what I felt on a visceral, blood-pumping level, and I discovered three sciences at work.

The first science was obvious: **Spiritual Science**. I have never felt God move so profoundly through my life. His presence and power were undeniable. But there was more, and the other two sciences were slowly coming into focus. I had a basic understanding of it, but I would need to dig deeper into the sciences of the mind (**Neuroscience**) and of changing habits (**Behavioral Science**). The spiritual awakening I felt in letting go of resistance on Resurrection Day was the first of the three keys to the combination that would unlock every door in my life.

♥ Heart-to-Heart

After reflecting on my life before Resurrection Day, I realized that resistance had kept me mired down in every ugly emotion describable: comparison, resentment, judgment, anger, frustration, and the list goes on. If the idea of letting go of resistance doesn't resonate with you, here are a few other ways to think about it: forgiveness, allowance, acceptance, non-judgment, peace, liberation, a calm knowing. Negative emotions had left me powerless to affect change in my own life. These awful emotions left me incredibly discontent, very sensitive to people's opinions and moods, and my feelings of inadequacy were enormous.

Sounds pretty miserable, doesn't it? Well, I wasn't miserable; I was human.

Before Resurrection Day, everyone I knew shared every one of my ugly emotions, and believe me, I know this for a fact because we talked about it all the time. We licked each other's wounds, and we talked about our pain. We lent an empathetic ear with no intention of finding a solution. We just wanted to sit in our misery a while longer and wallow a bit.

Are there people in your life that you get on the phone with, and you just wallow in your misery together? Or do you take to Twitter or another social platform and post a vague comment that invites hostile and negative fireballs between people, just for validation? Once my heart was reconditioned, it took a while to break the patterns with my friends and family. I lost friends because I would no longer "chew the fat" out of problems. If we weren't having a solution-focused conversation or a meaningful discussion, I was not going to participate in helping them keep their problems alive by feeding them more negative energy.

Letting go of negative emotions changed my life so profoundly; it allowed everything I had ever dreamed of to come flooding in. I realized that mindset was key. Positive thinking was the conduit to solutions, and negative thinking was the conduit to problems. That doesn't mean that problems do not exist; it just means that your attitude toward the problem has shifted.

Who knew that gossip and chocolate cake released the same hormones? When overdone and used as a coping mechanism, they are both toxic.

The shifts in my life were helping me have a clear understanding of the delicate connection between the mind, body, and heart. Have you ever had a moment, or even a day, where everything seemed to feel and flow right? I call this "Green Zone Living." It is an elevated place where you are focusing on feeling, thinking, and being inspired, loving, joyous, patient, and healthy. I was experiencing more and more Green Zone Living in my day-to-day life.

In my teachings, you are never more aligned to God than when you are in the **Green Zone** state of being. The gift of Green Zone Living is a direct connection to God, or your joy, in all its wisdom and glory. You are going to experience times in life when Green Zone emotions seem impossible—times when anger, fear, and heavy emotions weigh you down. Don't despair; my system will teach you how to move through the emotions without taking up residence there. They will become indicators of redirection and not permanent states of being. (I'll go into more detail about Green Zone Living and also introduce my emotional scale, which I call the **H.A.P.P.I.N.E.S.S. Ladder**, later on in the book.)

My life didn't completely change overnight after Resurrection Day, because learning to live happy took a little bit of practice. My heart was changed in an instant, but it took some time and retraining for my body, and my habits, to catch up. I grew to embrace my wobble with Green Zone Living; I recognized my wobble as the birthplace of discovery. Discovery would always lead me to recognize and identify tips and tools to reinvent a particular behavior. I no longer lived in judgment; I was solution-focused.

As I mentioned, there were two other sciences at work in my life, and I felt the harmony of movement between my heart, my inner peace, and my actions. My experience sparked a hunger for knowledge. I asked myself, *What in the world is happening to my family? How did we move from a place of chaos and desperation to a place of reinvention and strength?* I knew I was moved spiritually, there was no question about that, but what else was going on that made me so damn happy, and that made the lifestyle changes I had struggled with for years seem virtually effortless?

God had given me a mission to fulfill—one that was meant to go beyond my healing and my family's healing. To take His mission for my life from my dinner table to dinner tables across the country, perhaps even the world, would require a deep level of understanding of all that had happened to me, spiritually, biologically and behaviorally. It was time for me to become an even more committed student. I had dabbled in psychology in college, and I consumed everything I could get my hands on regarding self-improvement from a very young age.

Now it was time for me to invest "real time" in an education that would allow me to share my message with complete confidence in its ability to spiritually, biologically and behaviorally transform your life, as it had mine. I needed to understand each component thoroughly to flesh out my system. *What allowed me to hear God so clearly that day? What happened in my body's chemistry that flooded me with such ease and grace as I transformed my life? Why was my behavior so easily redirect*ed to serve me *where my entire life it had sabotaged me? How do I teach this system?*

Who knew a researcher lived inside of me! Like the story of the Genie in the Bottle, once I unleashed my inner researcher, there was no stopping her. I was prepared to identify, review, clarify, develop, collect and analyze everything I could get my hands on.

I interviewed over one hundred different professionals in the fields of spirituality, neuroscience and behavioral-cognitive science to carve out the system that was entrusted to me. I found neuroscientists to speak very technically, behavioral scientists to speak very theoretically, and spiritual scientists to speak very ethereally. This left me with quite a convoluted language to translate. With no formal training in the sciences, I invested well over 10,000 hours in discovery, dissection, comparison, and analyzing data. I learned their language, and then I created my own.

I belonged in this world of science, spirituality, and exploration, but I realized that my curiosity was my greatest gift and there is no expiration date on transformation. Every time I felt I was nearing a comprehensive understanding of how the mind, body, and spirit come together to affect change, I would discover another piece of data. If that data disturbed my current model, or contributed to it working more effectively, it had to be explored and either dismissed or integrated. I couldn't just walk away from anything I felt would make a meaningful contribution to this work.

So, I stayed the course until my discoveries began a pattern of looping themselves. And what I mean by that is new data no longer created a new category. It would fall effortlessly into a category I had *already* defined. This discovery was an indicator to me that my work was nearing completion, and the only thing left to do was translate these findings into a working curriculum that was easily understood in everyday life.

Ultimately, I found that each of the sciences has a place at the table, and together they make the perfect meal. Neuroscience is the protein. It provides the building blocks of tangible, measurable results. Behavioral Science is the carbohydrate. It directs energy and helps make the meaningful habit changes necessary for lasting change. And, Spiritual Science is the healthy fat that makes everything work together effortlessly. Psychology makes up 80 percent or more of our success (probably more like 95 percent, to be honest). So, leaving out the importance of psychology was never optional to me. However, the psychology I'm referring to is not necessarily the psychology taught at universities. My psychology is better described as mind-body-spirit integration or connection.

There are three ways that you may find yourself learning this material. (I find this information fascinating and I hope you do, too, but I want you to be aware that learning is a verb, and it is going to require your full participation. Knowledge is not enough.) Your subconscious mind is what is responsible for learning information.

3 Ways of Learning

The first way your subconscious mind learns is by **Hypnosis**. It is what happens during our young formative years under the age of seven. So, from the time we are in the womb up until about seven years old, we're kind of in a hypnotic state. During this period, a majority of the subconscious mind is programmed. We're taking in more information than we're putting out, so that we can acquire our survival skills. So, here's a thought: *What if we were raised by a fearful parent, or in an alcoholic home? How does that shape us? What if food was used as leverage for good behavior, or withheld for bad behavior? What if we were raised with five siblings, or we were an only child?* The combinations of "what ifs" are endless and, ultimately, we all have our share of desirable and undesirable subconscious programs. The good news is my system will teach you how to use your conscious mind to shift subconscious behaviors effortlessly without overhauling your entire subconscious mind.

The next way we learn is through repetition or **Habituation**. Now, this is typically what happens during our school age years, or our parental and social training years. This is a time in our lives that we learn our ABC's, how to drive, our manners, etc. We learn how to tie our shoes, how to ride a bike, make our bed and put away our clothes. These are all habitual practices that we do based on repetition. In addition to the subconscious mind developing our survival skills, it also is our habit mind. The most important thing about a habit mind is that habits are resistant to change, both good and bad. A compound known as **Neural Growth Factor** glues habits in place. This sticky process serves us by creating procedural habits; without this glue, we would have to relearn simple tasks over and over again. But it also makes breaking habits more challenging. The good news is my system will teach you, brain hacks, to replace unwanted habits with habits that serve you.

Finally, the last way that we learn information is through **Emotional Shock**. This is when a chemical is released in the body during trauma or joy and is so strong that our chemical state is unable to return to its former state. This results in instant change. My transformation took place through Emotional Shock, both when dinner died and on my Resurrection Day. My brain snapped both times and was unable to return to its former chemical state. However, your brain doesn't have to snap in order to experience transformation beyond your wildest expectations. The good news is my system will teach you to utilize the energy of your thoughts to create the change you desire without the need of emotional shock.

Overwhelmed yet? Hang in there! I know this information can seem entirely too "deep," but I will simplify the process in the following chapters. My system is broken into Six Pillars of Support and Four Phases of Transformation. It is simple enough to teach a child, yet profound enough to change your life.

I am going to teach you how to find simplicity in a complicated world by letting go of the past, accepting the present, believing in the future, and finding H.A.P.P.I.N.E.S.S. and joy in every step of the journey.

The Brain and its Chemical State

Your brain is a chemical factory, and your chemical composition is a result of two different sources: your **Senses** tell you what's going on in the outside world, while your **Emotions** tell you what's going on in the inside world. To a great degree, our emotions are generated subconsciously through our reaction to an event or other stimuli. Without our awareness, we are creating an internal chemical state of being by simply feeling. The chemicals that are produced as a result perpetuate more like-minded thoughts. Then we are caught up in a pattern of being constantly stuck in the same incident/response pattern. This is called a **Thought Loop,** and we are going to work together to break these destructive patterns.

Have you ever had an experience that you say changed your life? Well, in fact, it did; experiences *do* change our life, because they chemically alter our brain! Our life is interpreted through our five senses (six, if you include intuition); as a result, our brain produces an emotional chemical that imprints that feeling or event. How long it takes for us to let go of the emotion is known as the **Refractory Period**. Emotional intelligence is learning how to shorten the refractory period of negative emotions.

Someone that is unable, unaware, or unwilling to work on shortening their refractory period will continue to live in the past, and they will never evolve. They unknowingly create a life out of the filter from a single, negative experience. An experience that could have lasted only a moment becomes their permanent state-of-being.

Here is a real-life example of how the refractory period can impact our life...

♥ Heart to Heart

I have a friend that, due to a hormonal imbalance, suffered several miscarriages. She happened to be pregnant with her fourth child at the same time I was pregnant with my fourth child, but her pregnancy ended in miscarriage. We were as close as two people can be, and after the delivery of my son, I noticed that she could not even look at him.

At first, the sadness, anger, and frustration surrounding her miscarriage was understandable. But, her refractory period went far beyond a healthy mourning. The longer her mind bathed in the hormones of anger, frustration, and sadness, the more we noticed her overall attitude shifting. She seemed bitter and resentful toward many things. She was evolving into a person that she didn't want to be.

One day, I sat down with her and shared what I had been noticing. Thankfully, due to the strength and nature of our relationship, I could be very candid with her. She admitted her feelings of anger, frustration, and sadness surrounding my son, as well as any other child. She also noted those feelings were leaking into other unrelated areas of her life.

Our conversation led to her adopting her fourth child! Rather than just talking about her feelings, we started talking about solutions. Her shift in perspective released every negative emotion she had been experiencing. She was filled with love instantly, and although her adoption process was not free of struggle, her heart was whole and filled with emotions that pulled her forward in the way only creation can.

Your Mind's Impact on Your Life

Creation is everything. Everything you see around you was born of a Creative Mind. Think about it. The wheel is mechanical engineering plus creativity. A garden is horticulture plus creativity. A thermographic camera is radiation plus creativity. In every direction we turn, creativity is at the center of what we are seeing, perceiving, and experiencing. To activate and live your life dominated by creative energy, you must first learn to detach from outcome and fall in love with process. This freedom releases your mind from the rigid restraints of expectations and allows it to freely move through the realm of endless possibility.

Masters of creative thinking use their minds differently; they give birth to ideas, and then they move into three quadrants of thought. First, the **Disciplined Thinker** masters information. Second, the **Synthesized Thinker** utilizes information. Finally, the **Creative Thinker** is bold, innovative, and inventive; this combination makes things happen! When it comes to creating a vision of our **Desired Self**, many of us just don't invest the creative energy necessary. If we don't shape our life through our **Creative Mind**, our life will be shaped through our stress response to our environment, the **Survival Mind**.

Our Survival Mind is necessary and should be respected, but it should not drive your life. Learning to bypass the Survival Mind will allow you to thrive and not merely survive. The Survival Mind is grounded in impulsive and programmed responses (constant reaction to present triggers). Characteristics of the Survival Mind include dominance (dominate or be dominated), aggression, sex and seeking a mate, rigidity, obsessiveness, compulsiveness, worship, fear, submission and greed. These are beliefs, attitudes, and actions that limit growth. Most people go through life allowing their Survival Mind to form and shape their future, but through a simple shift in perspective, you can learn to quiet your Survival Minds egocentric chatter and awaken your Creative Mind. This shift in perspective will affect every area of your life and is the gateway to never-ending expansion and personal growth. Put a language to your dreams and realize them for yourself. If there is one thing in this life that you should protect above all else, it is your Creative Mind's ability to design your life. Not creating a vision is a decision that renders you ineffective.

Negative or positive energy is just energy, period. Our goal is to shape-shift negative energy into positive energy. An example of this is a tornado (**Negative Energy**) and a wind turbine (**Positive Energy**). Both use the same energy, but one is destructive while the other is useful. This shape-shift happens through our awareness. It is imperative you know how to redirect fear energy. The release of resistance is the first step in redirecting this energy.

As a young girl, I spent years experiencing life through great degrees of contrast; rich experiences, emotional volatility and unintentional discovery. However, the most important discovery of all was very intentional; I discovered the interconnectedness between experience, desire, ability, and joy. Surrendering into possibility opened my eyes to opportunity, where before, I had only seen limits. This meant I had the freedom to create a future in my mind free of my limiting beliefs.

My system will teach you how to embrace expansion through spiritual connectedness, the role your mind and brain play to support your expansion, and how to train your eyes to see opportunity. Finally, my system will teach you to embrace contrast as your greatest teacher, which will allow you to find joy in the journey despite the circumstance. Always remember that your perspective in life will determine your destination. It is the difference between being successful "in spite of" (Survival Mind), and being successful "because of" (Creation Mind).

In the next chapter, you will build your **Why Story** through a series of questions and answers designed to activate your Creation Mind and quiet your Survival Mind. The result will be a Why Story you can stand on and use as your motivation to succeed.

CHAPTER SIX
Your Why Story

The first thing to acknowledge before building your new empowered Why Story is that *everything you are currently living is due to the stories you have been telling yourself.* There may be some aspects of your life that are wonderful, while others are riddled with confusion and angst. It all circles back to the stories you believe about your life, whether you recognize these beliefs or not.

Most often it is not even *your* story; it is a story you inherited from the generations before you: family, friends, religious leaders, teachers, etc., all taking part in the molding and shaping of your young mind. Once you tap into the confidence that connects you to your spiritual awakening, you will proclaim, "I don't like the story I am living." When you step into that truth, and you own your power to write a different story and set a higher standard for yourself, that is when you can begin to embrace a new version of your life. This is the life you were designed to live.

Once you have seen a glimpse of how magnificent you were meant to be, there is no going back. The problem most people have is they do not recognize that they have the God-given right to be joyous and happy — not in only a few areas of their life, but in every area of their life. **Contrast,** or emotional discomfort, is actually the launch pad that will align you with the highest version of yourself. Understanding that contrast is the birthplace of your desires doesn't mean that situations won't arise in life that cause discomfort; it means that you will recognize that emotional discomfort is a signal that you are not in alignment with the highest version of yourself. Your only job is to line up.

When your focus shifts away from the contrast you are experiencing and on to the task of learning to line up, every day and every experience becomes a chance to get better and better at this thing called life. Whether it is weight loss, relationships, work, children, or finances, this shift will turn your problem-centric world into a world of creation and never-ending personal fulfillment that will delight you and allow you to find joy in every step of the journey.

How do you know you are living a life separate from your highest self, stuck in contrast, yet ready to grow? First, you are reading this book! You have a gnawing, a yearning, and a discomfort. Negative emotions may begin to feel, well, negative; whereas before this spiritual awakening, negative feelings felt normal, and you allowed yourself to live in that emotional space. When you are spiritually connected, and you begin perceiving life with endless possibility, it is difficult to settle for the old emotions. Your desire to be in alignment with who you were meant to be, your highest self becomes so strong that anything less in unbearable; and the feelings of emotional discomfort are your indicator.

Once you develop your Why Story, you will learn how to use your indicators, and you will rejoice in redirecting your life when emotional pain is present. Your indicators are your moment-by-moment guidance; they keep you moving toward the life you want to create while embracing the one you have. Because of the powerful fuel you created in your Why Story, you will embrace every challenge and change your life in a state of Joy and Inspiration rather than in a state of pain and suffering. This is the discernable difference between what I teach in my system, and what every other diet and lifestyle transformation program teaches. This is my message, my gift, to you. Change doesn't have to be painful — it should be a joyous creation meant to heighten our human experience.

You can create your Desired Self by connecting to your Why Story. Ultimately, pleasure and pain work together to create your story. Everything we do is to either move away from pain or move toward pleasure. Often the pleasure and pain drivers overlap, so this isn't a neat and tidy process. Your Why Story or the creation of your Desired Self requires the contrast that pleasure and pain provide. This is your first lesson in contrast and embracing it as a teacher.

Here is a harmless example of how pleasure and pain can get confusing and how easy it is to activate the wrong state of mind:

> *You wash your face in the morning because you want it to feel and look clean.*
> *-or-*
> *You wash your face in the morning because you don't want others to think badly of you for not looking clean.*

The phrasing of number one activates Creation. The phrasing of number two activates Survival. Think about it. Why do you want to lose weight? Once you cut through all the red tape, it boils down to one of two things, and be careful, because how you frame the answer makes all the difference in which state of mind you activate.

For example, you want to lose weight because:

A) You want to live a long, healthy life, or
B) You don't want to die.

Answer A activates Creation and feelings of love and gratitude. Answer B activates Survival and feelings of fear and loss. Answer A contributes to health and wellness, while answer B contributes to disease and death.

The way you frame your answer determines what operating system you activate. If you activate the Survival system, you are by default activating hormones that are catabolic. They create disease. They create incoherence between cells and wreak a tremendous amount of metabolic damage, all because your thoughts were not framed to activate the proper operating system, Creation.

Creating Your Why Story & Vision of Your Desired Self

Now, let's build a compelling, emotionally charged Why Story that activates expansion, health, order, coherence, focus, and energy — emotions found in Creation. We're going to do it by moving *toward* a vision, not *away* from one. We are internal storytellers, so our story has to move us into action. It has to resonate right at the heart level, and it has to align with our principles.

You can create a compelling vision of your **Desired Self** as it would look in your health and fitness journey (or any area of your life) and lock down your Why Story in the next five minutes with this simple formula. People with clearly defined visions for their Desired Self have five things in common: they know who they are, what they do, why they do it, what they need from it and how they will change as a result.

I want you to write down on a sheet of paper the answer to the next five questions. Your "what" is the activity. Your "why" is the reason for doing the activity, and your "need" is what you receive back from the activity. Typically, the need question is going to be an external need, like accountability.

1. Who are you?

2. What do you love to do to serve your health and fitness? (Remember, we are creating, so you may not be doing this yet. But, we are living in the world of possibility and opportunity, so be liberal with your dreams.) Do you love to workout, cook, jog, create, and play with your grandchildren? In other words, what does your life look like if you were to dream a perfect health and fitness life? Think about that.

3. Why do you do it? Think about why you do what you do. For example, if your "what" is teaching yoga, your "why" may be to stay in touch with the calm energy you found practicing yoga. Or, if your "what" is to eat healthily, your "why" may be to be a better role model for your children.

4. What do you want or need from this thing? Just jot down a few words of what you need for the "what" and the "why" to have meaning to you. For example, if your "what" is to teach yoga, and your "why" is to stay in touch with the calm energy you have found through practicing yoga, your "need" may be accountability and dedication.

5. How will you change as a result? How will you transform or change as a result of honoring the first four questions? For instance, let's go back to our yoga example. If your "what" is to teach yoga and your "why" is to stay in touch with the calm energy you have found through practicing yoga, and your "need" is that teaching gives you accountability and dedication, you will change by realizing a deep sense of honor and integrity.

Here are my answers for this exercise:

1. Who are you? Robin Shea.

2. What do you do? I teach people to reinvent their relationship with food.

3. Why do you do it? To share valuable life skills and pay it forward.

4. What do you need from it? Personal fulfillment and accountability.

5. How will you change as a result? I will feel whole and complete.

Now we're going to put this all together in a sentence. Here's mine as an example: **I teach people to reinvent their relationship with food through alignment with joy and happiness, paying forward what was gifted to me. This helps me feel whole and complete.**

This formula is so powerful because it forces you to look both inwardly and outwardly. It activates both hemispheres of your brain, which invites them both to the planning party. If your right hemisphere, which is Mr. Airy Fairy Dreamer (Creative), isn't supported by your left hemisphere, which is Mr. Pencil Pusher Architect (Analytical), then you're in internal opposition from the very beginning, and you cancel yourself out.

Another way to think of it is this: When my husband and I were building our home 14 years ago, I would sit on the concrete slab and design my house all around me. What did it feel like, look like? How was the functionality? Where did the kids drop their shoes and their book bags after school? How was I going to position our television? Every little detail I dreamed up in my mind. And I also had to run it past our architect to make sure it was doable. Once I got the nod from him, I knew it would happen. But if he gave me a reason why something could not be done, I would either fight for it and cause more problems, or I would let it go redesign around a new solution. Inviting *both* sides of your mind to the planning party and joining the Dreamer and the Architect from the very beginning is a smart strategy.

So, let's finish building our compelling, emotionally-charged story. One of the most difficult things to do when you have decided to reinvent your life is to address the questions that people will ask you about your transformation. On any level, transformation is a very vulnerable subject. Whether it's losing weight, stopping smoking, starting to exercise, or just breaking the fast food habit, change of any kind invites feelings of vulnerability. We feel exposed.

If the people around you are engaging in the same habits, how will you be able to break free? Sometimes we even choose not to change just to avoid being asked any questions or to avoid feeling like an outsider, but I want your Why Story to have so much emotional energy that you are proud to share it with anyone and everyone that asks. You will be so driven by your "why" that doesn't matter if others don't understand or agree with your choices. So, what do you say when anyone asks what you're doing to lose weight, break habits, or just improve your life and get healthy? You repeat the very last thing you called out.

- **If someone asks you why you no longer eat fast food**, you might say, "I want to live long and see my grandkids grow up," if your "why" is, "I take care of my health to enjoy my grandchildren so I can play, run, and enjoy them as they grow up."
- **If someone asks you why you started teaching yoga at your age**, you might say, "I honor my life by honoring others," if your "why" is, "I teach young students yoga because sharing the calm energy I found through practicing yoga honors my life, and by honoring my life, I honor others."
- **If someone asks you why you only eat treats twice a week**, you might say, "I balance my life to look and feel my best," if your "why" is, "I have healthy food boundaries and exercise to feel balanced. It

gives me energy and structure so I can look and feel my best."

- **If someone asks you what you do**, you might say, "I pay joy and happiness forward. If your "why" is, "I teach people to reinvent their relationship with food through alignment with joy and happiness, paying forward what was gifted to me."

The condensed version of your "why" becomes your building block for your epic story. For me, I pay joy and happiness forward. That's what I do. And I do that by teaching people how to align themselves with joy and happiness to transform their life. Once you claim who you are, define what you do, why you do it, what you need from it, and how it changes you, you have a defined Why Story. And by doing that, you have also created a crystal-clear vision of where you're going. You will not make decisions that are out of harmony with what you intend.

This little exercise has created the vacuum that will pull you to, but also pull you through. You are beginning with the end in mind, detaching from the results, allowing the process to unfold free of stress and unrealistic expectations. Like I said earlier, use this worksheet in the index as many times as you want, and work through it several times with various combinations. You will know when you have landed on the perfect Why Story, because you'll feel motivated and compelled to honor it.

💜 Heart to Heart

When I was a little girl, I remember watching my dad. He would get up before dawn to plan his day, and relive his day every night when he got home. His stories would captivate me, my mom, and my sisters. He told them with such passion and such joy. It was obvious he was an artist of people. I never felt called to get up before dawn to plan my day or relive my day once I returned home. And, I never once remember telling a story that held anyone's attention. For my dad, sales supported his highest idea of himself, gave his life order and purpose, aligned him for growth, connected him to his dreams, gave him energy and vitality, and reinforced that all things were possible. Because sales was so instrumental in his Why Story, even the setbacks were embraced with emotions found only in Creation. I did not get the same fulfillment from sales as my dad did, plain and simple.

However, he always assumed that I would go into sales. This suffocated me to the point of panic attacks.

> To me, sales was uncomfortable and awkward. Because of the personality similarities between my father and me, everyone would put me in a box: the box of a salesperson. Sales exhausted me, made me moody and withdrawn, narrowed my focus, and made me feel very limited and separate from possibility. Sales suffocated me in every way possible, and therefore drained me in every way possible. Because I was experiencing sales without a compelling Why Story, I experienced setbacks that further reinforced my misery.

How many of us spend an entire lifetime in a suit that doesn't fit all because, for whatever reason, we have never committed the time or the effort to create the vision of our Desired Self based on our internal guidance system or our emotions? Are you beginning to see why this process is so very personal and how building your Why Story is so critical to lining up with the activities that will lead you to reach your Desired Self? Before I go further with helping you create your Why Story, let me say that I am so grateful for my experiences. Although the suit of a salesperson didn't fit me well, it did give me the contrast that I needed to wear the suit that fits me today. And that suit fits me like an apron! You have to be brave to create your life. Creation is not for sissies. It requires you to bare your soul, which is a very vulnerable thing to do. Being brave is a prerequisite for change...for the better.

I have shared my most personal stories with you on these pages. Many of these stories were held inside the vault of my heart for years, afraid that sharing them would diminish me in some way. But, on Resurrection Day, these stories took on a new meaning in my life. They became the shoulders I stood on, the fuel that pulled me forward. The humiliation I feared in sharing these tender moments and memories, now pales in comparison to the glory of living my life in complete alignment with my joy. Once I dropped my victimhood and allowed my stories to minister to me, I knew I had to minister to others.

You needed to know how vulnerable I was to diet pills and anorexia. You needed to know that I grew up in an alcoholic home and that I have a son with ADD. You needed to know that I never felt worthy in my life as a young woman. You needed to know I abandoned my nutrition principles in a grocery store parking lot.

My story is your story, and my imperfection is your imperfection. My light shines because of my story, and because every day I choose to embrace a new challenge, my light only shines brighter. We all share failure, and failure will always be part of the process of expansion, but failure doesn't have to define you.

Let me teach you how to fail forward, learn from your mistakes, and fall in love with the journey. Transformation truly comes when you make the mental decision to be "all in" and allow it to infuse every area of your life. In Section Two, we'll talk about surrendering to possibility and making transformation happen...

SECTION TWO

Introduction to the Six Pillars

In addition to experiencing my transformation, I have interviewed hundreds of people who have lost weight and kept it off for years. They have reinvented their life or transformed themselves. When I began mapping these stories along with my own, I realized that each of us shared these six core principles, and they supported us and continued to support our transformation. We may have used a different language, but we were all saying the same thing. So, here is an introduction to the Six Pillars of Support.

A pillar provides strength. Now whether in the form of stone, metal, or wood, a pillar supports a structure in the form of architecture or in the form of someone or something that is an integral part of an activity, group, or community. Pillars create the foundation that anything can be built upon. These pillars are used to hold up the vision of your Desired Self. Here's an overview of the Six Pillars and the support that they will provide you.

Pillar One: Happiness - Finding Joy in the Journey of Transformation.
When we learn to change in a state of joy and inspiration, our transformation is tethered to those very emotions. Finding joy in the journey requires leaning into your discomfort and struggle and redefining what it means to you. When we learn this skill, when we learn to lean into the discomfort. We choose the operating system of Creation, rather than Survival. And we understand how to reframe our world to serve the highest idea of ourselves. Get ready — my system will teach you how to recognize your happiness, identify your two states of mind, survival, and creation, and how to move from the low vibrations of survival into the high vibrations of creation.

Pillar Two: Discovery through Journaling. Journaling leads to self-discovery and ultimately, self-awareness. The scarcity culture created by allowing impatience and blame to tempt us with diets that have no long term possibility for success can only be transformed by developing the most valuable skill of them all self-awareness. Get ready — my system will teach you how to journal for the sake of discovery, why suspending judgment is a powerful tool, and how to recognize your patterns of behavior (i.e. your triggers, when you are vulnerable and when you are experiencing empowered moments). You will also learn three goal-setting techniques that will keep you connected to your Why Story.

Pillar Three: Nutrition — Finding Your Forever Plate. We are all called to be accountable for our lives, and answering that call nutritionally means establishing healthy parameters around our food world. There are a variety of nutrition plans that are grounded in healthy practices. The key to maximizing any nutrition plan is making sure it meets several criteria. In this chapter, I will go over a few of the most popular nutritional plans and show you what to take into consideration. Get ready — my system will teach you how to select and live happily within a nutrition plan. I will also introduce you to my own nutrition plan, the *80/20 Lifestyle*, with which I have found success for 14 years.

Pillar Four: Fitness - Setting Healthy Fitness Parameters. The willingness to move blood through your body at an increased rate for a sustained number of minutes every day and adding mild resistance training to your routine is a great measure of commitment. This may mean a brisk 30-minute walk followed by light-weight lifting, or a hard-core weight lifting session, a game of tennis, yoga, Pilates, or spin. It could also mean going hiking, surfing, or golfing. The point is to incorporate movement into your life every day. This commitment is the birthplace of self-respect, discipline, and quality of life. Get ready—my system will teach you how to incorporate cardiovascular exercise and strength training into your daily life without the need to become a gym rat, Tough Mudder competitor, competitive tennis player, marathon runner or power lifter...unless you want to be! My system will teach you how easy it can be to move your body.

Pillar Five: Support. This is your emotional support system. If we are brave enough to leave our wheelhouse and expose ourselves to the harsh elements of the unknown, we must also be brave enough to lean into a community for a much needed respite. Being part of a community that shares the struggle, lends an empathetic ear, and provides constructive problem solving is invaluable. Get ready—my system will teach you how to identify your tribe, bless those that think they are lending support, and be impervious to those who try to sabotage your new commitment.

Pillar Six: Setting Your Expectations & Custom Goal Setting. People are tired of being defined by society's idea of perfection. Living dietless means we choose our own story over society's compulsory ideas. We choose to embrace our unique body type. Learning to embrace our unique **Somatotype** (body type) can be challenging because many of us internalize an external image of beauty that is not in alignment with our predisposed body type. This one thing can set us up for failure from the very beginning. Get ready— my system will teach you how to discover your unique Somatotype, embrace it, and build an image in your mind's eye that is in perfect harmony with your source.

With these six pillars in place, the journey to transformation is supported from every direction. Each pillar is unique and strategically selected to support areas of life that are susceptible to collapse. It is important to note that no particular pillar is more important than the others. In the next chapter, we will explore each pillar in greater detail and discuss how they will help you before you pick up the fork.

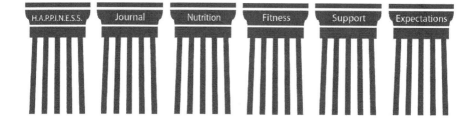

Chapter Seven
Pillar One: Happiness
Finding Joy in the Journey of Transformation

Now that I've given you the overview of the Six Pillars, let's take a closer look at each one, starting with my very favorite, Happiness. I emphatically believe that happiness is our reason for being. God provides us with emotions to guide us toward our highest self, yet so often we choose to stay mired down in emotions that are spiritually and physically destructive.

What does happiness look like to you? This should be an easy question, but it is not. It is a question that many avoid, or paint their answer with broad brush strokes simply because the answer is unrecognizable. If you feel unworthy of happiness, or if you have lost touch with what makes you happy, you may struggle putting into words what happiness means to you. Others have given up on happiness all together and lean into the universal word, "fine," which is actually code for, "Happiness is unattainable, so I will settle." I am not talking about complex happiness built on outcomes; I am talking about everyday happiness regardless of and unattached to outcomes. Happiness is about embracing moments and sharing love and detaching from the outcome this pure form of joy will change your life.

I spent many years chasing the idea of happiness, I was looking outside for something that lived inside. Although I had many happy moments, it never occurred to me that, with a little understanding, happiness could be my constant companion. It wasn't until I experienced my resurrection that I recognized the power, potency and guidance of my emotions. Emotions are our compass, always guiding us. In order for your compass to be effective, you must trust that you are worthy of feeling the high vibration emotions found at the top of the **H.A.P.P.I.N.E.S.S. Ladder**. Some people avoid change and stay mired down in emotions that are destructive or low vibration. This happens for two reasons. First, they are stuck in the habit of thoughts that trigger those emotions, and second, they do not feel worthy of feeling happiness.

My job is to teach you to climb the H.A.P.P.I.N.E.S.S. Ladder one emotion at a time; your job is to trust your compass. In addition to the H.A.P.P.I.N.E.S.S. Ladder, I can't wait to share with you how badly your body is craving happiness and how happiness will minister to your soul. Happiness is healing, purifying, and protective! Let's get started...

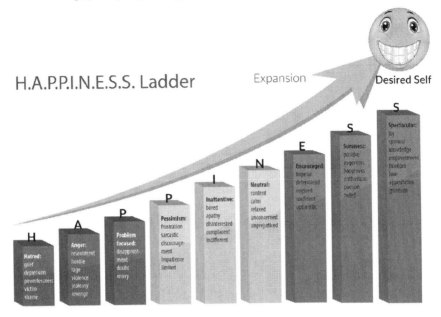

H.A.P.P.I.N.E.S.S. Ladder

Expansion

Desired Self

S — Spectacular: joy, spiritual, knowledge, empowerment, freedom, love, appreciation, gratitude

S — Sureness: positive, eagerness, happiness, enthusiasm, passion, belief

E — Encouraged: hopeful, determined, inspired, confident, optimistic

N — Neutral: content, calm, relaxed, unconcerned, unprejudiced

I — Inattentive: bored, apathy, disinterested, complacent, indifferent

P — Pessimism: frustration, sarcastic, discouragement, Impatience, limited

P — Problem focused: disappointment, doubt, worry

A — Anger: resentment, hostile, rage, violence, jealousy, revenge

H — Hatred: grief, depression, powerlessness, victim, shame

(All full color graphics are available for download at BeforetheFork.com)

To begin, you'll notice that the Desired Self or the Why Story rests at the top of the ladder. This is because it was created by joining your values, principles, desires, and dreams. You used both hemispheres of your mind to create a vision that you believe in (the Dreamer) and also felt possible (the Architect). You have the Dreamer and the Architect working together. Like I've said earlier in this book, the emotions found in the **Green Zone** of the H.A.P.P.I.N.E.S.S. Ladder have the most coherent signature, meaning their waves vibrate at a higher frequency.

Now, don't get all freaked out. I told you earlier that successful lifestyle transformation that is grounded in joy and happiness brings together three sciences: Spiritual Science, Neuroscience, and Behavioral Science. Well, this is part of the **Neuroscience of Change**.

Our cells have a language that is delivered throughout our body. The clarity of that language is dependent upon the cohesive-

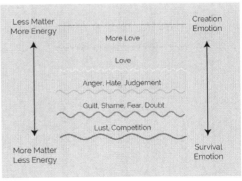

Less Matter
More Energy

Creation
Emotion

More Love

Love

Anger, Hate, Judgement

Guilt, Shame, Fear, Doubt

Lust, Competition

More Matter
Less Energy

Survival
Emotion

ness of its environment. The higher the vibration, the more the cells can communicate with each other. The lower the vibration, the more cellular discord, disconnectedness and confusion. Our emotions determine our internal vibration.

When we learn to elevate our emotions, not only do our cells more clearly communicate with each other, but our body also produces new hormones that release anti-aging properties—and who doesn't want that—plus advanced repair and restoration properties—again, another bonus. It boosts our immune system, and it also sharpens our intuition. That's just to name a few. Living in the Green Zone creates the ultimate coherent signature in our body, meaning we thrive and are in a state of wellbeing.

In addition to the Green Zone, we also have the **Red Zone** and the **Yellow Zone** as part of the emotional picture. Think of the colors as an emotional stoplight: Green is good to go; Yellow means caution; and Red means stop/danger. Emotions outside of the Green Zone create an incoherent signature, so anger, hatred, suffering, guilt, deprivation, shame, judgment, and jealousy, all create an incoherent signature between cells. As a result, this creates an internal environment that allows you to be become vulnerable to discomfort, depression, and disease.

Finally, let me say that the majority of us live in what I call the **Total Reactive Zone**. Meaning that because we have never thought of our emotions as our guidance system, we never valued the benefits of happiness; we simply live a reactive life. As a result, we have no knowledge of how to use our emotions as a navigation system. We are all over the ladder, hanging off like a monkey, at times. The second we find coherency, we lose it to circumstance. Our emotions are disorganized, and we experience highs and lows without the wisdom to frame each circumstance to serve us. We are so hot or cold that we are incapable of making well-thought-out decisions. As quickly as we are inspired, we are defeated.

Think of it like this: Do you remember the commercial from Verizon Wireless where the man just frantically walks around saying, "Do you hear me now? Do you hear me now? Do you hear me now?" Well, that is exactly what happens when we allow low vibrations to control our thoughts. We have no connection to our Desired Self because, remember, the Desired Self and the Why Story rest at the top of the H.A.P.P.I.N.E.S.S. Ladder. When we are experiencing low vibration emotions, we can't hear God calling us up to our ideas and dreams. Our connection is weak, distorted, and diminished. This disconnection makes everything we do both internally and externally more difficult, confusing, unclear and frustrating, not to mention the physical damage these emotions cause.

As a result, most often we quit altogether, become sick, or both. But when the signal is loud and crystal clear through our Green Zone emotions, the vision we created of our Desired Self and our Why Story silence all of the interference. We become solution-focused, determined, willing, coachable, and timeless. This is reflected in the production of hormones that support our transformation, both externally through our attitude and sharpening our focus, and internally through hormones that soothe and heal our bodies. I think this is God's way of saying, "If you seek love, understanding, patience, gratitude, and joy in all you do, I will create cohesiveness in your life that will keep my signal to you loud and clear." The scientifically proven connection between the high vibration emotions of love, understanding, patience, gratitude, and joy and cellular cohesiveness that results in elevated health is undeniable and proof that God wants us to live life in a state of Joy and Inspiration.

Transformation in a state of Joy and Inspiration is the ultimate goal!

Now, if you are freaking out about how you are going to learn to move yourself up the H.A.P.P.I.N.E.S.S. Ladder, keep reading because in this book I am providing you with the tips, tools, and techniques to master this beautiful practice of alignment.

Our personality dictates our personal reality, and our personality is a direct result of the thoughts we think and ultimately what we do with the energy created from the thoughts. Do we cycle the energy, repeating the thoughts keeping the energy alive. Do we dull out our thoughts in order to avoid the pain. Do we react too quickly and become volatile? Are we even aware that our thoughts are energy? The vast majority of us use our emotions as a response system, when it should be used as a guidance system. We live our lives unaware of the power of our internal compass. When we accept our thoughts as energy, and we learn to use our emotions as guidance, we can pull ourselves to and through any emotional situation.

Through my thirteen years of research, I discovered four distinct personality zones that people live in — not to be confused with the psychological personality inventory found in Jungian psychology, but zones of perceiving the world. Remember the quiz you took at the beginning of the book? Pull out your score—the zone you matched with is explained in this section. Get ready to take a deep dive into the personality zones...

The Four Personality Zones

1. Yellow Zone:

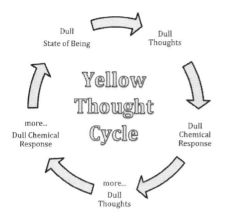

Yellow Thought Cycle

Dull State of Being → Dull Thoughts → Dull Chemical Response → more... Dull Thoughts → more... Dull Chemical Response → Dull State of Being

Characteristics of the Total Reactive:

- Yellow Zone: Proceed with Caution. Most of the time is spent indifferent. Leaning toward pessimistic thoughts with an occasional glimpse of hope. Lack of life force. Bleh.

- It's the process you've always used as it's convenient and takes no real effort. It's not horrible, but it's not great either. Status quo.

- DANGER ZONE: Status quo. It's mechanical. You're going through the emotions because there's no variance, which limits your life to expansion opportunities.

How do they feel and think, what are their chances of change and how does their body heal itself?

Yellow Zone Thinkers feel very little. They lean toward pessimistic thoughts with an occasional glimpse of hope. Yellow Zone Thinkers were often beautiful, zealous people once in their life, but through circumstance, have withdrawn into a world of dulled-out emotions. They have been worn down, disappointed, hurt, rejected, and embarrassed. Without the knowledge of how to use those low vibration emotions as guidance, they have withdrawn into a lackluster world. These Thinkers have designed a life to protect them from the thorns that they still hold onto. They are safe, but prisoners of their own protection; too afraid to feel, too afraid to try, too afraid of pain. Joy is for others, so they remain comfortably numb.

Yellow Zone Thinkers lack the ability to change because their desires are so weak. They are easily discouraged and impatient, so making a decision to change is rarely implemented long enough to make a difference. At the first sign of pain, they quit. They tend to be negative and accepting of conditions because they render themselves powerless. They settle for the status quo.

Yellow Zone Thinkers' ability to heal is stagnant. Dull thoughts create a dull chemical response, which leads to more dull thoughts and duller chemical responses. It is a vicious cycle that renders Yellow Zone Thinkers ineffective. All of the life force found in high vibration emotions is absent, and even if it is present it is so diluted that it is only doing a fraction of the good it could be doing. Their life is watered down and so is their body's chemical response. You know when you are sick and you can't taste your food? That is how the Yellow Zone Thinkers' hormones respond to their emotions; they lack potency.

Yellow Zone Thinkers - Good News / Bad News:

The good news is Yellow Zone Thinkers only have a few steps of thought redirection before they are living in the Green Zone. The bad news is Yellow Zone Thinkers have to embrace their thorns and allow themselves to feel again.

2. Red Zone Thinkers:

How do they feel and think, what are their chances of change, and how does their body heal itself?

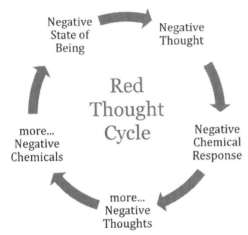

Characteristics of The Red Zone:

• Angry at everything. You have stability, it's just nonproductive and destructive to yourself and those around you.

• Can be considered a blessing as the emotions are typically 180 degrees, making this emotional state very easy to identify.

• With willingness for improvement, the guidance system is very clear.

Red Zone Thinkers feel everything with intensity, but their overall vibration is so low that the data coming into their senses rarely, if ever, elevates their thinking. They focus on their anger, problems, depression, etc. Red Zone Thinkers see conflict around every corner, they are defensive and argumentative, and are addicted to the chemical stimulus of these low vibration emotions. Every emotion on the H.A.P.P.I.N.E.S.S. Ladder will, and should, be felt by everyone at some point in life. It is through the contrast these emotions provide that we give birth to our vision; by knowing what we don't want we can more clearly define what we do want. The difference is, Red Zone Thinkers never attempt to elevate out of these emotions.

Red Zone Thinkers' ability to change is great if they would just turn 180 degrees and get out of their own way. Unfortunately, they are typically so stubborn and addicted to their emotions that their close-mindedness leaves them unwilling (or unable) to recognize opportunity. They are more concerned with validating their pain, anger, or despair than learning to elevate out of it.

Red Zone Thinkers' ability to heal is frighteningly low. It saddens me to say this but Red Zone Thinkers are more likely to manifest disease, whether it be physical, emotional, or relational. Disease is the result of interpreting the world through low vibration Red Zone emotions. Negative thoughts release negative chemicals which release more negative thoughts, etc. The toxic chemicals released through this thought cycle disrupt every operating system within the body. Their body's ability to heal, repair, restore, and replenish is completely diminished. The communication between cells is severely impaired, if not severed completely. Finally, the effects of this thought cycle go far beyond physical and emotional damage. Red Zone Thinkers can destroy relationships simply because their attempt at communication is made from the Red Zone. Even if their intentions are good, they lack the vibration to connect to others on a healing and loving level.

Red Zone Thinkers - Good News / Bad News:

The good news is Red Zone Thinkers are easy to identify, and if they choose to make the 180-degree shift they can be wildly successful and lead others to Green Zone living. The bad news is Red Zone Thinkers are stubborn, stuck, and cling to their excuses.

3. Green Zone Thinkers

How do they feel and think, what are their chances of change, and how does their body heal itself?

Characteristics of the The Green Zone:

· This process is ideal for your chosen environment, meaning it's in line with achieving your desired self.

· You're fulfilled. You're living a life of empowerment as every move is intentional. You are surrounded by the grace and beauty of a positive environment both internally and externally. Despite circumstances you are established in your positive disposition.

Green Zone Thinkers stay inspired and live life in a constant state of personal growth and expansion. This is not to say that Green Zone Thinkers are blissfully happy one hundred percent of the time, but it is to say that

Green Zone Thinkers perceive life differently. Every obstacle is opportunity in disguise, making life a wonderful dance between what is and what can be, resulting in falling in love with the journey. They move up and down the H.A.P.P.I.N.E.S.S. Ladder, experiencing every emotion the other Thinkers experience with one exception: They know all that their desire can be found at the top of the H.A.P.P.I.N.E.S.S. Ladder, and THAT the key to getting there rests in their thoughts. Their only goal is to elevate out of non-productive thoughts and into Green Zone thinking. They accept the climb, rung by rung, every day, and embrace tips, tools, and techniques that support their climb. Green Zone Thinkers know that feeling angry is better than feeling hate, so they allow themselves to feel the anger and they let go of the hate. They watch as their anger softens into disappointment and their disappointment soon gives way to discouragement. With each changing emotion, they recognize their skills to master their emotions as they are climbing up the ladder.

Their discouragement soon releases into being unconcerned, quickly followed by feeling hopeful. Hopeful leads them right into eagerness and eagerness births a new sense of empowerment. This process of climbing the ladder can take a day, a week or just one moment sitting with your thoughts, once you have mastered the skills.A Green Zone Thinker embraces their emotions as their compass, and recognizes God's will for us to be joyous. They practice every day to surrender into the higher vibrations in order to stay connected to their source.

Green Zone Thinkers' ability to change is a calling on their heart and is complete before they ever get started. Everything they do is tethered to the high vibration emotions found in the Green Zone, meaning that even their failures nourish them because they allow failure to minister to their growth. They embrace change on a completely different level than any other Thinker. They feel connected, empowered, and supremely guided. They have released themselves from the constraints of a timeline and they have fallen in love with the journey of polishing up their life.

Green Zone Thinkers' ability to heal themselves is overwhelmingly optimistic. In addition to the positive impact of Green Zone emotions, the process of redirecting thoughts plays a large role in the release of chemicals that contain medicinal benefits as well. The healing art of positive thought is an ancient practice steeped in each and every religion practiced on earth today.

My religion is Christianity, but every religion I have studied seeks the same beautiful connection to the source within. Our physical bodies (brain, nervous system, endocrine, and immune system, lymphatic system, etc.)

share a common chemical language with our emotional body, and when we consciously choose to experience life through the elevated emotions of the Green Zone, our bodies are rewarded chemically (as well as spiritually) with a boosted immune system, improved heart health, reduced stress, elevated self-esteem, reinforced habits, and more.

Green Zone Thinkers - Good News / Bad News

The good news is Green Zone Thinkers are the happiest people on earth! Bad news is...there is no bad news! And if there was bad news, Green Zone Thinkers could and would turn it around.

4. Total Reactive Zone Thinkers

How do they feel and think, what are their chances of change, and how does their body heal itself?

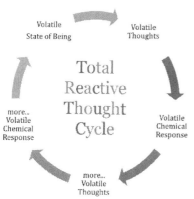

Characteristics of the Total Reactive:

- Completely disorganized. Living life through circumstance, not intentionally living. Reactive response living has no intention. Ultimate victim mentality.

- DANGER ZONE: You have high highs and low lows, so you have a lot of opportunity for emotional dependency. There's a great variance between your emotions. Emotional adrenaline junkie.

- Junkies off toxic emotions. Addicted to gossip. Bullying. Bashing someone else's life or lifestyle.

Total Reactive Zone Thinkers are in a state of emotional chaos. I fear to say that the majority of us live in the Total Reactive Zone. Although we may naturally be a happy person, if we live without the awareness of our guidance system, we fall victim to the Total Reactive Zone. Total Reactive Zone Thinkers move in and out of the Red, Yellow, and Green Zone with complete emotional dependency. Total Reactive Thinkers have high highs and low lows and are very emotionally dependent on external circumstances.

Total Reactive Zone Thinkers' ability to change is as volatile as their thoughts. One minute they are all-in and the next they are soothing themselves with destructive habits due to their inability to use their compass. This lack of emotional stability renders the Total Reactive Zone Thinkers impotent.

Total Reactive Zone Thinkers' ability to heal themselves often cancels itself out. Green Zone moments release endorphins and serotonin only to be canceled out by Red Zone moments that release adrenaline and cortisol. The dance between zones is metabolically destructive. This cycle of volatility leaves them vulnerable to disease, emotional distress, and strained relationships.

Total Reactive Zone Thinkers Good News / Bad News

The good news is Total Reactive Zone Thinkers know what it feels like to be happy. The bad news is it is difficult to break the toxic pattern of emotional addiction. **Question: Are you willing to embrace change, be patient and forgiving of yourself, and allow yourself to be a beginner?** If you answered "yes," then you are ready to move forward regardless of the zone you identified with most closely.

Stop Spinning Your Plates

I love the image and idea of the plate spinner. She is effortlessly spinning all areas of her life simultaneously in perfect harmony. But, if you've ever watched the art of plate spinning, then you know she started by mastering one plate at a time. Take the idea of "mastering one plate at a time" and think about it for a moment. Life requires all of us to spin dozens of plates, but how many of the plates we are spinning have we actually mastered? Here is your opportunity to slow down and focus all of our energy on one single plate, the plate of your nutrition. You will be amazed at how focusing on the mastery of one plate can positively impact every other area of your life.

It is important to understand that no one strictly lives in one zone. We move around the zones depending on the circumstance. For example, you may light up in the Green Zone with joy and happiness when you talk about your children, but when the subject of your ex-husband is brought up, you immediately drop into the Red Zone. So, identifying the zones and where you "live" in any given moment, regarding any given subject, is where you begin. Knowledge is power, and an emotional understanding of the H.A.P.P.I.N.E.S.S. Ladder is ultimate power.

Once our compelling Why Story is clearly defined, and we have the knowledge of how to use our emotions as our navigation system, we can break the cycle of Red, Yellow, and Total Reactive Zone Thinking. It is easy to identify the Thought Cycles of others, but not as easy to determine your own.

What's most important is that you recognize that <u>you</u> control what zone you are in—not the other way around.

The H.A.P.P.I.N.E.S.S. Ladder is an incredible tool for every area of your life. I use it daily in my ongoing effort to align with my Green Zone emotions, but Green Zone emotions alone will not transform your life. There is no elevator to the top of the H.A.P.P.I.N.E.S.S. Ladder—you must climb one rung at a time. You can't expect to jump from anger to love; that is too big a leap. Moving from anger to disappointment is a realistic step, and disappointment is only a small step away from hopeful, and hopeful is only a small step away from joyful. You have to pull yourself up the ladder, rung-by-rung, emotion by emotion, recognizing the progress you are making.

To change a habit (thought habit or physical habit), you have to break neural pathways and create new ones. Green Zone Thinking is spiritual and will tether your change to positive emotions, but change itself is a behavioral and neural process. Once you spiritually line up your emotions with the changes you want to make, you are ready to move into breaking the unwanted thoughts and behaviors and replacing them. One final thought on happiness before we proceed: learning to redirect your emotions our of the Red or Yellow Zone to elevate your life experience is a life-long practice. This is the art-of-living a joyful life.

In the Tips, Tools, and Techniques section at the back of this book, I offer skills to help guide you through the process of climbing the ladder, soothing destructive emotions, and harnessing the power of positive energy to pull you forward in your health and fitness journey.

But, before we even begin to talk about what is going to go on your fork, we have to address the pen that is going to go into your hand...

I am a pretty easy person to get along with. I have generous boundaries and I am very accommodating. However, in matters of principle, I stand firm like the mighty oak—and Pillar Two is a matter of principle. This pillar is especially important to me because it is a quantifiable measure of how committed someone is to transform.

I run a small personal training business, and each day I teach classes and counsel my students. In addition to that, I take out the trash, clean the bathrooms, and wipe down the equipment. This is me working "in" my business. Other times I stand back, assess what is and is not working, how things can improve, and what needs to be eliminated. This is me working "on" my business.

Journaling is working "on" your life.

This particular pillar is the quickest and most effective way to gather and measure information for use in your personal growth. It is also a very accurate indicator of how committed someone is to transformation. It asks the following questions:

Do you really want to change?

Do you want to achieve your health and fitness goals?

Are you willing to do whatever it takes?

Will you commit to getting "real" with yourself—even if it feels uncomfortable?

Journaling is a non-negotiable requirement for the clients who work with me. I have turned down clients from my studio because they were unwilling to examine their habits through journaling. Breaking destructive patterns of behavior (such as the destructive thought cycles of Red, Yellow, and Total Reactive Zone Thinking and their destructive behavioral habits) and replacing those patterns with more empowered behaviors is a combination of Neuroscience and Behavioral Science. The emotional fuel charging the change is Spiritual Science.

If you were to stop reading before this chapter, your takeaway would be: "Get happy and everything will work out." But the truth is, learning to navigate the H.A.P.P.I.N.E.S.S. Ladder alone does not change behavior, but it does accomplish three very important things: First, it makes you fall in love with the journey! There is no destination worth going if the price is your happiness. Second, it actually makes you healthier. Happiness is the groundwork for all health; energetic, biological, neurological, chemical, and hormonal. Third, it tethers your change to positive Green Zone emotions. This is important because change can take place either in a state of joy and inspiration or in a state of pain and suffering...and the end result is not the same.

Choosing to change in a state of pain and suffering looks something like this:

Diet of the Day = Pain: This entails grasping at the next trendy diet, clinging to a number on the scale, and spending all your emotional energy in a state of self-loathing and disappointment. Diets alone don't work and they cause a tremendous amount of emotional and physical damage. The statistics say it all: Diets alone have a 98% failure rate.
Poverty Mentality = Pain: People with this type of mentality spend their life in a state of lack, never feeling they have enough. A thought-cycle rooted in poverty breeds jealousy, resentment, worry, depression, ans so on. Poverty is no way to live, and it's an attitude, NOT a state of finance.
Communication Breakdown = Pain: The number one problem in any relationship is effective communication. A slight shift in perspective can deepen every relationship in your life.

When change takes place in a state of pain and suffering (unhappy dieting, poverty mentality, or argumentative relationships), catabolic hormones are released and are tethered to the change. These catabolic hormones trigger the body's fight-or-flight response. Although we are designed to move effortlessly between our operating systems — "fight or flight" and "rest and digest" triggering "fight-or-flight" irrationally, without the threat of "real" immediate danger, we cause our body to get locked into the "fight or flight" position, resulting in chronic stress. Chronic stress limits our ability to downshift into the parasympathetic nervous system, or "rest and digest." It can result in serious health conditions including anxiety, insomnia, muscle pain, high blood pressure, and a weakened immune system.
You can change in a state of pain and suffering, break habits, and learn

to act differently, spend differently, or eat differently, but without the emotional alignment found in the Green Zone, the changes are tethered to the hormones found in the Red and Yellow Zone. Your thoughts may or may not elevate to release the Red and Yellow Zone emotions, but why take the chance? Line up your emotions first to ensure your change is tethered to the life affirming hormones found in happiness.

This brings me back to journaling. How can you change patterns of behavior if you do not recognize them? I spent months journaling my experience; months journaling my failures, successes, lessons, and goals. I chronicled every step of my process without a clear understanding of the power and wisdom I would find at the end of my pen. Talk about self-discovery! I had no idea of the patterns of behavior I was so deeply rooted in, until the very end. Without that knowledge, I could have never redirected my behavior, built my toolbox, and recognized destructive patterns as well as empowered moments. I would have been less likely to honor the daily prayer I prayed over my journey, focus on my goals, and use the tools of process and projected imagery. Journaling was more than instrumental in my transformation; it was my coach! It was me working "on" my life, not "in" my life.

What journaling is not: A romantic idea of capturing your life for posterity.
What journaling is: An instrumental pillar of change.

After years of journaling, I have come up with a template for journaling that is very effective. Now, before we dive into each part of the journaling process, let me make one thing clear: journal pages shouldn't take any longer than 15-20 minutes per day. If you enjoy the process, then spend as much time as you would like. The idea is to not blow this up bigger than it actually is and get overwhelmed. These are simple practices with profound results, not complicated practices with complicated results.

Once you launch into my program, you will commit to daily journaling for a 28-Day Experience. In my research, I discovered a variety of reports and opinions as to the time required to break old habits and replace them with new ones, ranging from 21 days to as many as 245 days. However, I found a 28-day cycle to be the perfect amount of time to experience every hormonal fluctuation that a human experiences, break and form new **Synaptic Connections** (weaken unwanted habits and form new habits), and work through each of the Four Phases of Transformation.

Your daily journal pages consist of the following areas: Daily Blessing, Mental Rehearsal Practice, Nutrition, Fitness, Support, and Expectations. Let's examine these closer...

Part One: Daily Blessing

You will recite a daily blessing or mantra over your journey. The words chosen for the blessing are specifically designed to activate your Creative Mind and deactivate your Survival Mind. The blessing is this:

> *This is my journey.*
> *My thoughts determine who I am, what I have, and what I can do.*
> *The power to decide my life rests inside of me through the Holy Spirit and I boldly claim my right to live with grace and glory on my side.*
> *My thoughts will reflect a love for myself only equaled by God's love for me.*
> *My mind is alert.*
> *My heart is open and joy and happiness are my guiding lights.*
> *Amen.*

This little prayer sets the tone for your day and it lets you know that everything you're doing to move closer to your Desired Self is blessed. When I reclaimed my family's nutrition, I was empowered to face and overcome any obstacle life threw at me. I knew I was chosen for this work and I had every intention of being an obedient steward. I created this blessing as a way to connect me to the energy I felt so viscerally that day in the hallway. I don't just say the words, I try to *embody* the words. I reflect on the H.A.P.P.I.N.E.S.S. Ladder and focus all my energy in the Green Zone. This prayer of blessing over my life is a daily reminder that all I desire to be, do, and have rests in my ability to live in a state of joy and inspiration.

Part Two: Mental Rehearsal Practices

Everyone has different motivators that ignite their health and fitness fire, but have you ever really stopped to think about harnessing the power of different types of motivation? That's right—there are different types of motivators, and I'm going to show you how to harness the power of each type. We have already established in the previous chapters that the single most important component in successful lifestyle transformation can be found in the mind. Guess what? Your motivators (and de-motivators) also live in your mind.

We are going to learn how to engage your motivators and disengage your de-motivators by using a past, present, and future approach, or what I call: Lesson, Launch, Lead and Life.

Tapping into your unique motivators is important, but it can be challenging. What fires up one person may actually de-motivate another. As with most things in life, this is not a one-size-fits-all category. Your motivation is unique to you, and discovering what will affect change in your mind is the goal. Who cares what fires up anyone else; how does that help *you*? Let's selfishly focus only on the things that move your heart into action!

Mental rehearsal includes four types of Mental Practice: **Reflection** (Lesson), **Catalyst Goal Visualization** (Launch), **Process / Performance Visualization** (Lead), **Projected Visualization** (Life).

The reason Mental Rehearsal works lies in the fact that when you vividly imagine yourself reacting and overcoming certain situations, you are creating neural pathways in your brain, just as if you had physically performed the action.

The key to using Mental Rehearsal is knowing how and what to imagine. There are two main guidelines for productive Mental Rehearsal or Visualization and Imagery:

1. Regular Practice - Schedule a time for your daily visualization and imagery practice. Begin by visualizing two or three times per day—morning and evenings while in bed is a good time and place to start. Begin with 5 minutes of visualization. As you become more skilled, and relax into the practice, you will discover that you may want to carve out more time to visualize for the sheer pleasure of the practice.

2. Keep Thoughts Purposeful and Directed - This will lead to a positive experience. Learn to direct and control the images in your head. Let the mindless chatter enter in and exit out; do not pay attention to it. The more you practice, the more skilled you will become at controlling your visualization technique.

Important side note: the more sensory components you add, the more real the visualization (or experience)! See, smell, touch, taste, and hear your experience for maximum impact.

I mentioned there are four different types of Mental Rehearsal. Let's look at each one in detail:

Reflection and Projected Imagery (the Lesson and the Life)

Red, Yellow, Total Reactive and Green Zone emotions have one thing in common: they are all energy! Red Zone emotions are the most destructive and vibrate at the lowest frequency, followed by Yellow Zone emotions, with Total Reactive Zone emotions being a toss-up. And, of course, Green Zone emotions are the superheroes of emotions. Nevertheless, all emotions are energy and can be harnessed and used to strengthen your commitment to creating your Desired Self.

Think about a tornado: Red Zone energy, destructive, unpredictable, unforgiving, and deadly. Now think about a wind turbine, which is total Green Zone energy. A wind turbine captures kinetic, disorganized energy from the wind, redirects it, and turns it into mechanical energy. We are going to learn to become wind turbines and convert Red and Yellow Zone emotions into Green Zone Energy.

An effective reflection and projection practice will intensify your desire to reach for your Desired Self by exacerbating the reality of your choices. In other words, reflection is "worst-case scenario" and projection is "best-case scenario." But you must understand that negative thoughts are powerful, and take root quickly. Because of their low vibration, negative thoughts create a denser vibratory field. This is why negative thinking sticks around easier than positive thinking. Negative thoughts are sticky, slow, heavy and create a great deal of resistance. This is in direct contrast to positive energy, which is lighter in vibration. Positive emotions move quickly, more easily, and with less resistance. Knowing this, and other components of quantum physics, I want to share a few guidelines for using reflection and projection effectively.

Reflect and then Project, in that order. Science has shown that concentrating for less than seventeen seconds on a thought will prevent it from becoming chemically active. Spend no more than seventeen seconds on your reflection to keep it a passing thought rather than a nagging thought. Seventeen seconds is enough time to generate the polarity of emotions needed to reinforce your projected practice, meaning you become clear on what you do not want to happen, but not enough time for the negative thoughts to take hold.

Now on the flip side, your Projection should be the opposite of your Reflection. Your projected image should last no less than ninety seconds. During that ninety seconds, it is important that you embody each and every emotion, create your images in color, and incorporate as many senses as possible. The idea is to flood your body with the positive hormones found in the Green Zone. Ninety seconds is the minimum time required to create hormones potent enough to deepen the effect of the projected imagery practice. Here is an example of a Reflection/Projection practice:

Focus: Imagine your desired future and play scenes in your head, like a movie. First negative, followed by positive.

Reflection: Picture yourself in your twilight years. You are sixty or seventy years old. What does your life look like? See it and feel it like you are watching a black-and-white movie. Reflect on what your life will look like if your desired changes are not made. Paint the picture as dark and melancholy as possible, but remember to limit your exposure to images and thoughts to seventeen seconds.

How will your life affect your family?
Will you be able to play with your grandchildren?
Are you on oxygen from smoking or taking daily shots for diabetes?
Have you lost limbs due to diabetes?
Do you have a preventable lifestyle cancer?
Has your lifestyle already cost you your life?

Projection: Time to switch gears! Take the same scenario you are sixty to seventy years old and you embraced the changes necessary to redirect your life. See it and feel it like you are watching a big screen production in full color and sound. Paint the picture as viscerally as possible and remember to keep the emotions and feelings alive for a minimum of ninety seconds.

How will your lifestyle changes impact your family?
Will you be riding bikes, coaching, swimming, or jogging with your grandchildren?
Are you vibrant and full of enthusiasm and love of life?
Are you exploring new adventures?
Are you gardening, traveling, or climbing mountains?
Are you in full appreciation of your twilight years?

One thing to keep in mind while practicing Reflection/Projection is this: Reflection activates your Survival Mind; Projection activates your Creation Mind. Reflection is negative; Projection is positive. We never want to run *from* something (Reflection); we always want to run *to* something (Projection). The contrast between the unwanted (Reflection) and the wanted (Projection) is what will take your life to the next level. The contrast this process provides is the birthplace of strong, life-changing desire.

Practicing Reflection/Projection together is not always necessary. You can create such a vivid image of how you want life to be, look, and feel that creating contrast each time is not necessary. I found the more connected I became to my chosen future, the less I needed to be reminded of the unwanted one. But every now and then it is very helpful!

Visualization side note: Researchers have discovered that certain people struggle with visualization. Do not be too literal regarding the term "visualization." It doesn't mean to strictly see with your mind's eye; it is meant to include sight, sound, touch, smell, and taste. It is an all-inclusive experience inviting every one of your inner senses to participate. Whether you experience your visualization practice through a single sense (Visual, Auditory, Kinesthetic, Olfactory or Gustatory), or any combination of the senses, it is irrelevant. As long as your inner experience is, "Yes, I am in absolute love and alignment with this creation," that is when visualization has the power to transform your life!

I found my ultimate strength through my Reflection/Projection practice. Although I utilized each type of Mental Rehearsal regularly, Reflection/Projection allowed me to make my healthy lifestyle transformation about more than just aesthetics. My transformation became deeper and more meaningful to me when I created a future life for myself that centered around my ultimate desire, and that is to live a life that allows me to be active well into my twilight years.

When I began my Mental Rehearsal practice my children were only 10, 7, 6, and 2. Although grandchildren weren't even on the radar, they were very much part of my Reflection/Projection practice. Today, 14 years later, my first grandbaby is here. I am so grateful I paved the way, spiritually and physically, to enjoy the life I created through my commitment to happiness. This "Tanana" (my grandmommy name) is looking forward to embracing every moment of my grandson's life.

Process/Performance (the Lead)

I unintentionally discovered visualization right after my Resurrection Day. If you remember, I abandoned my family's dinner table and was raising my children on fast food. Small children can be relentless when they are denied their cravings. Fast food is specifically formulated to create cravings, both physical and emotional, through sugar, high fat, convenience, and even branding (think of the toy in a Happy Meal). Breaking my children's addiction to fast food was not easy, and it forced me to get very creative. Every time we got in the car and drove past one of our previous fast food restaurants, the boys would start begging: "Please, just this once, we won't ask again...please mommy, please, please." They were a team; they never got along more brilliantly than when they were trying to corrupt my commitment to their health.

One day, I remembered a cassette tape I had listened to when I was in my late teens, and I recalled the techniques it used to help change habits through visualization. Using that as my inspiration, I went to work constructing a visualization practice for my children. I used leverage from our weekly 20% indulgence.

Here is what I did: When the boys and I would get in the car, I would ask them what special weekend treat they wanted. I really built it up. Each one of them would chime in and describe in detail what they wanted to spend their weekly 20% indulgence on. I had them describe how it tasted and smelled. Were they going to help shop for it and help me prepare it? Why was it their favorite treat, what did they love so much about it? Then we would try and combine everyone's ideas into a special meal. I made sure the special meal we were going to create was fresh on everyone's mind every time we drove in the car. Occasionally the boys would notice an old fast food hang out and break into their begging song, to which I would calmly say, "Really? Y'all want to give up what we have planned for the weekend for a stupid hamburger? Seriously? Okay, if y'all don't want to make homemade chicken and dumplings with Texas sheet cake and homemade vanilla ice cream for dessert, that's your choice..."

All of the boys would pause, scratch their heads, and one by one say, "Nah...we want the chicken and dumplings!" Every now and then one of the boys would say, "YES, give me the hamburger," but it would have to be unanimous, and typically the other boys would be able to talk that one kid off the ledge! Before too long, they just stopped asking. We would peacefully drive by fast food places and even the famous "Golden Arches" would go unnoticed. They even began to tell other kids, in a matter-of-fact-way, that they didn't eat fast food. The cycle was broken!

That was my rudimentary attempt at piecing together my limited knowledge of Behavioral Science over fourteen years ago. Turns out that limited knowledge was actually the beginning of me discovering a very powerful technique that has been used for decades with elite athletes: Process/Performance Visualization.

Process/Performance Visualization is a two-part strategy: Situations that inhibit success (process) and things that enhance success (performance). In either case, visualizing yourself using the tools to either redirect a pattern or create a new pattern will assist you in achieving the new desired behavior. Set yourself up to succeed each day by spending a few minutes focusing on process and performance techniques. Here are examples of each strategy:

Process - For process preparation, the focus of, mental rehearsal should be on factors that interfere with success, such as obstacles or activities i.e., breaking patterns by redirecting behavior.

Performance - For performance preparation, the focus of mental rehearsal should be on factors that can enhance performance, such as motivation or activation; i.e., creating patterns by visualizing success.

The line between Process and Performance can sometimes blur and isn't always clearly defined. Don't worry about that; just remember, you are either redirecting or creating patterns. Don't try and correct every area of your life all at once — just focus on one thing at a time. When you begin seeing results, you'll be inspired to focus on more areas.

Here are three examples of Process/Performance in real life. (Remember, you will only pick one tool and focus on utilizing it.)

Process Example #1:
Breaking your daily Starbucks addiction to a mocha frappachino (500-1,200 unnecessary calories). How do you overcome this destructive habit?

Tools:
- Reroute your drive away from Starbucks.
- Picture yourself passing by without stopping.
- Picture Starbucks in calories and not coffee.

Process Example #2:
Breaking the pattern of joining your co-workers for an over-indulgent lunch.

Tools:
- Pack your lunch.
- Bring your walking shoes and walk one mile during your lunch hour.
- Invite a co-worker to join you walking.
- Hear yourself turning down the invitation, politely but firmly.

Process Example #3:
Breaking the pattern of a nightly bowl of ice cream.
Tools:
- Eat a protein rich dinner.
- Reduce bowl size.
- "Ride the wave": Go to that place in your mind that feels the pleasure of the experience without actually eating. This is often enough to satisfy the craving.
  — 10 Minute Pause: Don't deny yourself the craving, simply state to yourself, "I will revisit this impulse in 10 minutes." This is typically enough time for you to gain control over the impulse. Not denying yourself outright tames the human primal response to denial, which is feast or famine.

Performance Example #1:
Creating a new morning routine of waking an hour earlier to do yoga.

Tools:
- 3-2-1 Launch: Imagine yourself hearing your alarm and immediately going into a 3-2-1 Launch countdown; on 1, you spring out of bed.
- Go to bed earlier to make up for the sleep you will be losing.
- Feel the satisfaction of your yoga practice.
- Get an accountability partner.

Performance Example #2:
Creating the habit of purchasing healthier items in the grocery store.

Tools:
- Never shop when you are hungry.
- Only shop the perimeter of the grocery store.
- Carve out time to go grocery shopping three times each week and keep the trips short and specific.
- Never shop without a list.

Performance Example #3:
Creating the habit of drinking at least eight, 8-ounce glasses of water every day.

Tools:
- Experiment with different water bottles (glass bottles, bottles with squirt tops, different sizes etc.).
- Flavor water with fresh orange, lemon, lime slices and mint.
- Find the right temperature you enjoy drinking.
- Fill a large container with the amount you want to drink and pour it into your smaller container. When the large container is empty you are finished.

Important: It is not enough to jot down strategies; you must strengthen your mind with the visualization practice. Just jotting down strategies is like buying the healthy food and never eating it, or buying the weight set and never using it! You must engage your mind in this practice in order for it to work. What is happening in your brain when you visualize is a whole lot more than you might think. The chemicals produced and the electrical impulses felt in visualizing the behavior are identical to those that would be released if you actually performed the behavior. You are creating the new behavior by simply seeing yourself accomplishing it.

Process/Performance Visualization is situation-specific, and requires custom strategies for each individual. Think outside the box; you are gathering tools and then picturing yourself using these tools to support your efforts. Later on, you will have the opportunity to practice these tools in the 28-Day Experience where we will walk hand-in-hand through my system and a complete transformation cycle. I've also created an index at the back of the book full of helpful tips, tools, and techniques to help you get your creative juices going.

Many hours of research went into developing this facet of my system. I interviewed sports psychologists, behavioral therapists, religious psychologists, and many more, and they all overwhelmingly support the use of Mental Rehearsal in shaping new behaviors. In addition to third party confirmation, I personally have felt the power of this practice It works!

Part Three: Nutrition and Exercise

The first question you must answer is this: Are you just trying to lose weight, or are you wanting to transform the way you eat for reasons far beyond the scale? Reasons that go beyond your physical appearance, such as: breaking family patterns of diabetes and obesity; minimizing your risk for cardiovascular disease and certain lifestyle cancers; setting a better example for your children and providing them with healthy nutritional boundaries; break the vicious cycle of toxic food cravings; or finding a contentedness within your relationship with food and fitness in addition to looking and feeling your best?

Losing weight is a worldwide obsession and packaging up "diets" and "fitness" crazes is big business, with each diet and exercise program claiming to be "the best." The truth is that no one diet and no one exercise is best for everyone. The results of diet and exercise programs are always measured in pounds, when I feel they should be measured in joyful sustainability.

This is why I chose "clean eating," or what I like to refer to as **First Generation Foods** as my nutritional guidelines. I consider a diet and fitness program a success when healthy weight loss is achieved, is sustainable, and overall physical activity is enjoyed.

- DO: Eat whole foods, lean protein, vegetables, fruits, nuts, and seeds
  DON'T: Eat processed foods, sugar, dairy, and grains

- DO: Eat anything grown organically from the ground
  DON'T: Eat anything derived of an animal

- DO: Eat unlimited amounts of protein
  DON'T: Severely limit carbohydrate intake

- DO: Eat very high carbs and minimal protein
  DON'T: Eat fat (10% or fewer)

- DO: Balance each meal with split of protein/carbohydrate/fats
  DON'T: Eat high-GL carbohydrates

Here are a couple of popular fitness trends that are the current rage:

- Wearable technology
- Body weight training
- HIIT (high intensity interval training)
- Strength training
- Group training
- Yoga
- Functional fitness
- Outdoor activities

- Smartphone apps
- Personal training
- Spin classes

Bottom line: There are a ton of ways to structure your health and nutrition world, and there are pros and cons to each of them.

I am not going to tell you which approach is best for you. Whatever weight loss and exercise plan you decide upon, for the sake of your journal pages, honor the plan and the parameters it places around your food and fitness. The journal pages provided in the back of this book are general so that you may utilize your chosen plan.

Part Four: Building Your Toolbox

What do binge triggers, travel, going out to eat, hunger, fatigue, stress (among others) have in common? They can all derail your efforts to stay-the-course. The only way to overcome these saboteurs is to create a strong and well-equipped toolbox.

Building your toolbox, however, does more than just create solutions for struggles. It strengthens your brain's ability to shift out of problem mode and into solution mode more easily. When we change our perception of failure from "defeat" to "opportunity," we activate our Creation Mind and quiet our Survival Mind. However, in order to keep our Creation Mind activated, the phrasing of our lesson-learned is equally important. The lesson-learned is the take-away. It is where we plug-in a new behavior in order to avoid future mistakes.

The tool you design as a result of the lesson-learned must be a tool born of Creation. This is another example of how we tether change to positive emotions, and consequently hormones, found in Green Zone Thinking. It is easily achieved through incorporating a daily practice of **Event/Stumble/Tool Thinking (E/S/T)** through journaling.

E/S/T Thinking is a form of **Metacognition**, or "thinking about thinking." Beginning your day with a goal of monitoring your behavior in search of E/S/T opportunities elevates your thinking and engages your prefrontal cortex (consciousness). Through consistent and dedicated journaling, you will develop a greater degree of metacognition. This will result in your ability to identify obstacles quickly, and develop "tools" or strategies more effectively; it also supports the acceptance of flexibility when designing and refining tools. A well-established E/S/T Thinker is always eager to identify another new tool or strategy that can be more effective in achieving their goal. E/S/T Thinkers are more aware of their strengths and weaknesses and design tools that specifically address their unique set of challenges.

The goal on your journal pages is to go through the day looking for areas of improvement and, when something pops up, immediately thinking of ways to be better prepared next time rather than wallowing in the perceived failure. For example: You go to the grocery store on an empty stomach and you leave with cookies, pastries, and ice cream. Let's look at how this will play out on your journal pages, and remember to be conscious of Creative Thinking versus Survival Thinking.

Creative Thinking:
*Creative Thinking identifies the Stumble and builds a Tool.
EVENT: Grocery shopping on an empty stomach
STUMBLE: Rampant impulse purchases
TOOL: Eat a small meal or snack 30 to 45 minutes before grocery shopping.

The goal is to build your toolbox with custom tools designed to enhance your strengths and minimize your weaknesses.

Survival Thinking:
* Survival Thinking identifies the Stumble only.
EVENT: Grocery shopping on an empty stomach
STUMBLE: Rampant impulse purchases
TOOL: Never go grocery shopping on an empty stomach

Do you see the difference? Creation provides a specific tool, phrased in a positive way; while Survival provides no tool, and is phrased in a limited, restricted way. So, to summarize, your toolbox has two parts: **Observation** — i.e., identifying the event and stumble, and **Strategy** — identifying the lesson and designing a tool from Green Zone Thinking.

Journaling is an essential ingredient in the secret sauce of success. Later in the book, I'll lead your through specific, well-designed journal pages that ground you in your principles (the Blessing), provide exercises that support change in a state of joy and inspiration (Mental Rehearsal), create accountability through specific nutritional and physical requirements (Nutrition and Fitness), and promote countless growth opportunities by developing E/S/T Thinking.

When should you journal? As often as possible. Every time you pick up your pen and jot down a thought, you are engaging your prefrontal cortex and your Creative Mind. Every time you engage your Creative Mind, you are strengthening your new neural connections. Begin your day by reciting the Blessing and setting your intentions, and then check-in periodically throughout your day to perform mental rehearsals, note nutrition and exercise, and list any E/S/T moments. At night, wrap with a summary of your day.

Doing this every day will train you into living in twenty-four hour blocks, meaning that, at the end of each day, you will wrap-up that day (good, bad, or indifferent), put a bow around it, bless it for the learning and growth opportunities it provided, and give it away. It is over...never to be lived again. You only take into tomorrow the victories, lessons and tools, nothing else.

Every day you are a work-in-progress, so think of it like this: If you had a hobby you loved, let's say cooking, and your oven broke, would you continue putting your dishes in the oven to cook? Of course not! The oven breaking is actually a gift, because you have no other option but to repair or replace it. But what if your oven just didn't heat evenly and everything you cooked burned on one side? For a period of time you would adjust your cooking to your malfunctioning oven, because that's what we do! We adapt to our environment without realizing that we can actually *upgrade* our environment all together. You are effectively upgrading your life. You aren't fixing a broken oven, you are replacing the entire oven with a new convection model complete with self-cleaning button, and Wi-Fi option!

When you identify what doesn't work and/or that there is a better way, you leave the broken and ineffective ways behind you. Emotions are no different. Red, Yellow, and Total Reactive Zone Thinking are broken tools. Whenever you carry guilt, shame, discouragement, disappointment (Red, Yellow and Total Reactive Zone emotions) from yesterday into a new day, they will sabotage you every time. When we feel the low-vibration emotions found in the Red and Yellow Zone, our Primal Brain responds by taking over and directing us to known self-soothers; this is done to release the feel-good hormone oxytocin. Oxytocin is a wonderful hormone, but the mammalian care-giving system (Primal Brain) is not a good judge of self-soothers.It only knows what it knows. If eating an entire chocolate cake has released oxytocin in the past, it will try to comfort you with cake.

That is why journaling is so very important. It is the "best" way to keep you engaged in the process of change, help you build new empowered habits, redirect your primal mind's need to self-soothe, and more. My journal pages are specifically designed to encourage change through a state of joy and inspiration. Now, let's take a look at nutrition in more detail...

Chapter Nine
Pillar Three: Nutrition — Finding Your Forever Plate

I recently conducted an informal survey on my Robin Shea Facebook page where I asked my followers four questions:
1.) How many diets have you been on in the last five years?
2.) Did you lose the unwanted weight?
3.) Did you keep the weight off?
4.) Did the diets become your "forever" eating plan?

As I suspected, the responses overwhelmingly support the national data that reflects DIETS DO NOT WORK.

About 95% of all dieters who successfully lose weight by following a prescribed diet will regain the weight (plus some) in 1-5 years. And, since your body fights for your survival, overly-restrictive diets actually *slow down* your metabolism which makes it more difficult for you to lose weight. Fad diets can be harmful because they often lack essential nutrients and teach you nothing about healthy eating. And, more often than not, they boomerang you right back to your unhealthy eating habits. This begins the cycle of "yo-yo dieting," which can lead to a scale obsession which is a gateway to eating disorders. And finally, pills, potions and lotions are usually the next line of defense against unwanted pounds. (Remember my Fen-Phen story from the beginning of this book?)

Dieting, most often, is a toxic cycle born out of a lack of knowledge of how to redirect behavior, embrace healthy nutritional parameters, and adopt a completely new lifestyle. I have faithfully and joyously lived the *80/20 Lifestyle* for the past 14 years. When I created this lifestyle all those years ago, it was in an effort to reclaim my family's dinner table, elevate our nutrition, and provide my children healthful parameters in which they could grow and thrive, despite living in a fast food world.

Before we go further I think it is important to point out that there is no one-size-fits-all diet. Every situation is unique and must be given consideration. For example, losing weight was very important to me but not as important as nutritional integrity and family integration. Whatever I did, it had to serve my family and teach my children healthy nutritional parameters — not just be about weight loss. As a result of a slow and steady approach, I achieved my weight loss and have been able to maintain my weight for over 15 years. It may have taken me a few months longer, but I did not have to compromise good nutrition in the process. My priorities were clear:

1.) Nutritional Integrity
2.) Family Integration
3.) Weight Loss
4.) Lifestyle Diet

However, as you have read earlier, there were times in my life that I simply wanted to be skinny—period. My priorities for those years may have looked like this:

1.) Weight Loss
2.) Fast
3.) Easy

Although the *80/20 Lifestyle* answered all of my prayers relative to finding my balance nutritionally — and is the nutritional tool I use to coach my clients and help them redefine their nutrition, reclaim their health, and meet their weight loss goals — I would never be so arrogant as to claim that the *80/20 Lifestyle* is the ONLY DIET that works. The fact is, that is just not true! There is value and efficacy in any diet plan that meets your nutritional goals, and that you find alignment and joy in following.

The reason this book is titled, *Before the Fork*, is because there is a certain amount of ground-work that must be done before you ever begin a new diet program. If this groundwork is approached with careful consideration, your chances of success could rise from the national average of 2% up to as high as 80% or better—the groundwork is that important! My in-depth study of a variety of diets was anchored in my own knowledge plus the impartial information found at *U.S. News*, which evaluated 38 of the most popular diets in 2017 and identified the best. I found the information in this article impartial, thorough, and well presented. Learn more at: https://health.usnews.com/best-diet.

Below, I will present an overview of several leading diets, including special considerations like whether the diet is a paid membership, and if it offers an online and/or mobile support. I will then rate the diet based on six (6) categories using a star-system (1 through 5, with 5 being the highest). The plans will then be given an overall rating based on the collective stars for each category. Be sure to look at each individual rating as the collective may not be as important as the individual rating for your needs. For example, if a plan is expensive and scores 1 star in affordability, but the cost is not of concern to you, then that score is irrelevant. Match yourself to the best plan for your individual needs.

I used slightly different criteria for my rating system than what was used in the *U.S. News* article. I have developed my own unique insight as a teacher, and as a practitioner of lifestyle transformation for over fourteen years—there is value in both view points and I encourage you to investigate thoroughly for yourself.

Seven Categories:
- Affordability
- Ease of Following
- Nutritional Integrity
- Short-Term Results
- Long-Term Results
- Family Integration

The diets I will be reviewing are:

- Weight Watchers®
- Jenny Craig®
- Paleo Diet®
- The *80/20 Lifestyle Diet*

Weight Watchers: 3.6 out of 5 Stars

Membership	Support			
	In-person	Online	Mobile	Personal Coaching
✓	✓	✓	✓	✓

Overview:

In the early '60s, Weight Watchers founder, Jean Nidetch, invited friends to her home in New York to discuss how best to lose weight. Since then, that group of friends has grown to millions of women and men around the world who come together weekly to help each other meet and exceed their weight-loss goals. Weight Watchers' goal is to help you lose weight (up to 2 pounds weekly) while also putting a spotlight on behavior in an effort to develop better habits. Losing weight while living healthier is at the heart of Weight Watchers.

According to Weight Watchers, every food has value. Weight Watchers created a point system called SmartPoints®to score each food based on calories, saturated fat, sugar and protein. Foods that cost the most points are foods that are higher in saturated fat and sugar, less nutritionally dense, and the least satiating. Foods that are the least in points are foods that are higher in protein, more nutritionally dense, and fill you up the longest. As a result, the Weight Watchers SmartPoints® System is a clever calories-in versus calories-out system. Each person's SmartPoints® are calculated based on their individual goals.

Weight Watchers success relies heavily on support provided by in-person meetings, online chat or phone calls from people who have lost weight using Weight Watchers. These are people who have kept the weight off and have been trained in behavioral weight management techniques. Anyone participating in a Weight Watchers program has access to an online feature that allows them to chat with an expert familiar with the program at any time, 24/7.

✓ Affordability: The only fee related to participation in the Weight Watchers is selecting the program that best fits your budget. They have a variety of programs to offer ranging from "Onlineplus" at $19.95 per month, to "Total Access" at $69.95 per month. Weight Watchers has no food items to sell; they encourage members to choose foods they want, can afford, and enjoy. They have found this to be key to long term sustainability.
  o Pros: Weight Watchers offers a variety of price points which make this program affordable for most everyone.
  o Cons: Many individuals are weary to commit to monthly payments.
  *** 3 out of 5 Stars

✓ Ease to Follow: Weight Watchers has eliminated virtually every bit of confusion around developing and tracking new nutritional patterns.

Weight Watchers provides several options for tracking your food intake and keeping up with your SmartPoints® including their mobile app, website, barcode scanner, Apple Watch and even a handy pocket guide and/or pocket calculator. Add to that the thousands of (free) online recipes, restaurant guide, alcohol allowance, cooking tips, and emotional support offered through online and/or in-person group meetings, and Weight Watchers longevity, and very high compliance rate is understandable.

- ○ Pros: Flexibility to create your own diet. No foods are off-limits.
- ○ Cons: There is a necessary learning curve that weeds out those who are committed and those who are not ready to commit very quickly.

****4 out of 5 Stars

✓ Nutritional Integrity: Weight Watchers has no indications of serious risks or side effects arising as a result of following the diet plan. Weight Watchers encourages independent food selection based on the guidelines provided in the SmartPoints® System. As a result, much of the integrity of the nutrition will ultimately be left up to the participant. But, by simply following the SmartPoints® System, the participant will be making more balanced and overall healthier choices. Weight Watchers suggests taking a multi-vitamin daily.

- ○ Pros: Weight Watchers provides many options to help maintain nutritional integrity.
- ○ Cons: Ultimate nutritional integrity is going to be the responsibility of the participant.

***3 out of 5 Stars

✓ Short-Term Results: Weight Watchers utilizes a calorie-in versus calorie-out model for weight loss, in addition to nutritional balance. Therefore, initial weight loss may be a bit slower than other plans that utilize another weight loss model. On average, Weight Watchers participants lose 6 pounds after the first four weeks.

- ○ Pros: Slow and steady weight loss makes for greater long-term success.
- ○ Cons: Initial slow weight loss can often be discouraging to participants.

***3 out of 5 Stars

✓ Long-Term Results: Weight Watchers regular weigh-ins and group meetings greatly contribute to the overall success of the program and longevity of participation. In a 2013 study in the *American Journal of Medicine*, Weight Watchers researchers found overweight and obese participants assigned to Weight Watchers were nearly nine times more likely to lose 10% of their weight than participants who were only provided printed materials and publicly accessible websites and tools for weight loss. The more active a participant is in utilizing the tools, forums, and accountability measures, the more successful they are.

> o Pros: Weight Watchers has an overwhelming track record of long term sustainability.
>
> o Cons: None.

*****5 out of 5 Stars

✓ Family Integration: Raising a family within the boundaries of healthy nutritional parameters is as much about modeling behavior as it is about nutrition. Children and young adults require a variety of nutritional considerations in order to grow and develop, but more importantly, they need role models. Children will absorb the eating habits and attitudes demonstrated within the home. Weight Watchers provides a general framework for healthy nutritional parameters; however, the integration of the framework into the family dinner table is very dependent on the attitude in which it is presented and carried out. It has great potential to effect positive change in families and break unwanted habits.

> o Pros: Weight Watchers provides generally healthful parameters that, if followed properly, can enhance family nutrition, break unwanted habits, and introduce healthy boundaries.
>
> o Cons: An unhealthy attitude toward a nutrition program can do more harm than good to children who model the behavior of their parents or in-home caregivers.

****4 out of 5 Stars

Jenny Craig: 2 out of 5 Stars

Membership	Support			
	In-person	Online	Mobile	Personal Coaching
✓	✓	✓	✓	✓

Overview:

Jenny Craig was started in Melbourne, Australia, in 1983 and was brought to the United States in 1985. Jenny Craig uses a scientifically-proven, balanced approach to weight loss utilizing its own team of registered dietitians and expert Science Advisory Board. Two pounds a week is the goal for a Jenny Craig participant. In addition to Jenny Craig's prepackaged meals — which help you to lose weight by restricting calories, fat and portions — Jenny Craig also promotes an active lifestyle and behavior modification. By combining personalized meal and exercise plans, plus weekly one-on-one counseling sessions Jenny Craig participants build healthy habits in a supportive environment.

It offers two programs: "Standard" and "Jenny Craig for Type 2" (which is a specialized program for those people with Type 2 diabetes). The length of the diet is determined individually based on desired results, and it could range from three months to three years. Participants spend the first half of the weight loss program eating prepackaged Jenny meals and one snack a day. Once the participant is half way to their goal weight, they'll begin cooking for themselves twice a week using Jenny's recipes. Once goal weight is reached, the next four weeks are dedicated to making all your own meals, and adjusting to a slightly higher number of daily calories, plus regain prevention strategies.

Jenny Craig is a calorie-in versus calorie-out diet plan with very inflexible guidelines however, they do factor in a "splurge strategy," allowing up to 250 extra calories for special occasions. The Jenny Craig "Anywhere" program makes one-on-one support easy by providing walk-in locations, phone and even video chat opportunities. During these counseling sessions participants and consultants review progress, discuss obstacles, and choose the next week's meal selection.

- ✓ Affordability: Expense is the major reason many dieters avoid the Jenny Craig program. Members pay a $99 enrollment fee and a minimum of $19.99 a month for the "Jenny All Access" program. If you are only interested in consultation each week, you can pay $39.00 a month for the "Jenny As You Go" month-to-month option. Neither of the programs include food—the average food cost is $15 to $23 each day, plus shipping costs.
  - o Pros: If you have the budget to absorb the expense, this may be your ticket!
  - o Cons: This is a cost prohibitive diet for the vast majority.
  *1 out of 5 Stars

- ✓ Ease to Follow: Variety, taste, and convenience make Jenny Craig a delicious, mindless way to lose weight. Portions are small, but they do not skimp on flavor. Once participants shift into preparing their own meals, Jenny Craig offers hundreds of free, low-fat recipes on Jenny's website. Jenny makes eating out a viable option and encourages you to discuss with your consultant to create a viable menu. Alcohol in moderation is acceptable, and Jenny even offers celebration-friendly drinks options. Jenny offers on-line meal planning, progress tracker, activity tracker, food journal tools, and even a mobile app to track on the go. All of Jenny's prepackaged meals are created with satiety in mind, meaning Jenny's meals are structured to keep you feeling fuller longer.

- o Pros: Reliable quality and variety with an integrative system that weans you off of the packaged food.
- o Cons: It may be too easy to follow. If participants can afford the program and the meals, the motivation to assume responsibility for the knowledge necessary to be independent of a program is diminished, leaving them dependent on the program.

*****5 out of 5 Stars

✓ Nutritional Integrity: Jenny Craig has no indicators of serious health risk or side effects. However, they do limit participation in their program to people older than 13 and no one with milk, wheat, or soy allergies. There are a few positive cardiovascular indicators related to the plan, and Jenny Craig also offers a Type 2 diabetes program. Jenny Craig is recognized as a diabetes prevention program. Jenny Craig does recommend vitamin supplementation.

- o Pros: Jenny Craig follows a variety of guidelines that ensure the nutritional integrity of their prepared meals according to several government agencies.
- o Cons: Although Jenny Craig's prepackaged meals pass many government standards, if the participant is interested in eliminating additives, artificial ingredients, added sugars, and hydrogenated oils (i.e., trans fats), Jenny Craig should be avoided.

***3 out of 5 Stars

✓ Short-Term Results: Jenny Craig uses a calories-in versus calories-out model for weight loss, so if you are committed, you will lose weight on the plan. The caloric structure of the weight loss plan, coupled with encouraging physical activity, lend to a jump-start on weight loss.

- o Pros: No guesswork, ease of delivery, no calculating.
- o Cons: No guesswork, ease of delivery, no calculating. What is Jenny Craig's greatest advantage is also Jenny Craig's greatest disadvantage for growth.

***3 out of 5 Stars

✓ Long-Term Results: Although not as high as independent weight loss programs, Jenny Craig has a remarkable level of long-term adherence.

Out of all of the commercial weight-loss programs, Jenny Craig participants lost the most weight over 12 months. The key to Jenny's success may be in the prepackaged food and the psychological support provided through various streams.

- o Pros: If you work the program long-term, you will be exposed to the success strategies that are independent of the prepackaged foods.
- o Cons: Reliance on prepackaged meals home-cooked meals and restaurants are not easily adapted to the plan, expense.

***3 out of 5 Stars

✓ Family Integration: The key phrase in the Jenny Craig system is "personal." This is not a plan designed to integrate into the family dinner table. Children model behavior, first and foremost, and they will absorb the attitudes and eating habits of the nutritional role model of the home. Therefore, participation in a Jenny Craig program in a home with young, impressionable children needs to be taken seriously.

- o Pros: None.
- o Cons: Without a strong nutritional plan in place for the family, the potential for damaging a young child's perception of nutritional is a real threat with a commercial program.

0 out of 5 Stars

Paleo Diet: 1.3 out of 5 Stars

Membership	Support			
	In-person	Online	Mobile	Personal Coaching
		✓		

Overview:

The Paleo Diet is derived from the philosophy that our modern society could benefit by returning to the roots of nutrition followed by Paleolithic man (more than 10,000 years ago). This is pre-agricultural revolution, which means no refined sugar, dairy, legumes, and grains.

Paleo participants follow a simple idea: if the cavemen didn't eat it, you shouldn't either. The theory is that participants may lose weight, prevent unwanted disease and live an overall healthier, fitter, disease-free life. Paleo experts feel the culprit behind our greatest health problems can be found in society's obsession with highly processed foods and carbohydrate-heavy eating patterns. Paleo advocates are convinced we will heal our health if we eat as hunter/gatherers, i.e., animal protein and plants.

Most information, guidelines and recipes, relative to following the Paleo Lifestyle can be found online. However, there are also several books that present the Paleo framework. Basic Paleo principles offer three "levels" that allow for different degrees of flexibility: three "open meals" per week on the "entry level" plan, two on the "maintenance" plan, and one on the "maximal" plan. Participants choose their level and are free to move between levels as they feel beneficial.

Because Paleo does not offer organized support groups, membership programs, personal coaching, etc., the success of the program relies heavily on a personal honor system. There is no calorie counting on the Paleo Diet, but entire food groups are eliminated.

- ✓ Affordability: Because Paleo is grounded in animal protein and fresh produce, it may be expensive.
    - o Pros: Fresh food.
    - o Cons: Could be cost prohibitive.
  **2 out of 5 Stars

- ✓ Ease to Follow: Although the principles are simple enough, diets that restrict entire food groups are difficult to follow in the long term. A number of great resources are available for recipes, and eating out is acceptable as long as you keep it basic (meat and veggies). Alcohol is not permitted on a true Paleo diet, but hybrid forms of the diet make some exceptions. This diet is easy to follow in theory, yet challenging to follow in execution.
    - o Pros: Simple, understandable guidelines
    - o Cons: Entirely too restrictive for the vast majority
  *1 out of 5 Stars

- ✓ Nutritional Integrity: Experts agree that the Paleo Diet is lacking nutritional integrity. Dieters are challenged to get all the nutrients they need while following the plan. Some experts consider the Paleo Diet unsafe.
    - o Pros: None.
    - o Cons: Lacking nutritional integrity.
  0 out of 5 Stars

- ✓ Short-Term Results: If participants track a "calorie deficit" while using the Paleo plan, they will lose weight quickly. This is due, in part, to the restriction of carbohydrates. A typical daily consumption of carbohydrates is 45% to 65% of total food intake; however, on Paleo that drops to 23%. Carbohydrates store water molecules, so the initial weight loss

Before the Fork

will be a great degree of water weight, but it is weight loss nonetheless.

- o Pros: Want to fit into that tiny black dress for an upcoming event? Paleo may be your ticket.
- o Cons: Initial weight lost is water weight.

*** 3 out of 5 Stars

✓ Long-Term Results: Losing weight on Paleo is going to require calorie deficit tracking. The main concern is the consumption of animal fat and the long-term health implications. In several studies, Paleo-style diets yielded slightly higher long-term weight loss results versus low-fat diets. However, the omission of entire food groups leaves experts overtly skeptical.
- o Pros: Long-term weight loss is achievable.
- o Cons: Compromised nutrition and long-term health implications can make the Paleo diet a dangerous diet plan.

*1 out of 5 Stars

✓ Family Integration: Is Paleo a food trend or is it here to stay? Either way, the eating plan does have merit in that it eliminates refined sugars, and processed foods; but the elimination of grains, dairy, and legumes is of concern. Family nutrition is about providing a healthy framework for all members of the family to grow and thrive. Experts are opposed to integrating this diet into a child's daily nutrition.
- o Pros: The elimination of refined sugars and processed foods.
- o Cons: The nutritional imbalance, rigid guidelines and expense.

*1 out of 5 Stars

80/20 Lifestyle: 4.3 out of 5 Stars

Membership	Support			
	In-person	Online	Mobile	Personal Coaching
✓	✓	✓	✓	✓

Overview:

The *80/20 Lifestyle* was created in 2004 by me, Robin Shea, after searching for a way to bring my family back to the dinner table, break unwanted fast food habits, and build a healthy nutritional framework in which to raise my family. Since that time, the *80/20 Lifestyle* has blossomed into a holistic approach to losing weight and reclaiming overall health through a commitment to practical nutrition with an emphasis on behavior modification and emotional alignment.

The goal of the *80/20 Lifestyle* is to help each person and/or family build a healthy nutritional framework in which they can thrive, meet their weight loss goals healthfully and elevate their overall nutritional intake. This is achieved by following one of three eating plans or flexing between plans as needed, making the *80/20 Lifestyle* a "forever" nutritional platform.

All the guidelines for the *80/20 Lifestyle* can be found in my book, *The 80/20 Lifestyle Diet*. The basic concept of the *80/20 Lifestyle* is keeping nutrition 100% clean and healthy 80% of the time, while allowing participants to indulge 20% of the time. The term 80/20 is loosely interpreted and may cause confusion to those not familiar with the three different eating plans. The *80/20 Lifestyle* offers "Slow & Steady," "Rapid Results," and "Maintenance." Each plan allows for a slightly modified structure of the 80/20 concept.

While participants are honoring their 80% Healthy side of life, they must follow strict guidelines that eliminate processed foods, additives and preservatives. The term "First Generation" foods is used to describe the quality of nutrition that fits into the 80% Healthy side of life, meaning foods straight from nature with the least amount of human contact. No foods are off-limits, but careful consideration must be made when selecting. The reality is not all foods or brands are created equal; the *80/20 Lifestyle* has created a simple way to qualify each food source making sure it falls within a good, better, best framework. 80/20 even takes into consideration demographic constraints, financial limitations, and overall independent acclimation.

The *80/20 Lifestyle Diet* is growing in popularity and, as a result, the platform is expanding to include community memberships, in-person, on-line, mobile, and personal coaching opportunities, as well as retreats starting Summer 2019.

- ✓ Affordability: The only expense to participate in the *80/20 Lifestyle* is the purchase of the book, and perhaps this companion book, *Before the Fork*. None of the fee-related components of the lifestyle are necessary, although they are beneficial.
  - o Pros: The *80/20 Lifestyle Diet* provides a sturdy framework, affordable framework to reclaim your nutrition.
  - o Cons: Eating fresh, unprocessed foods requires more trips to the grocery store, so the time element in the beginning may take some acclimation.
  - ****4 out of 5 Stars

- ✓ Ease to Follow: The *80/20 Lifestyle Diet* provides a clear structure to operate within. First, the lifestyle is stripped down to the bare basics so the concepts are more easily digested, and then it begins expanding to include daily integration into a real-world dynamic. The *80/20 Lifestyle* works in conjunction with the *Before the Fork* framework which means behavior, attitude, and joy are at the forefront of this lifestyle diet.

- o Pros: Simple, understandable and achievable with a positive approach.
- o Cons: Participants must allow themselves to be a student, dedicated to the practices in both the framework of the *80/20 Lifestyle Diet* and the *Before the Fork* system of execution.

****4 out of 5 Stars

✓ Nutritional Integrity: Without a doubt, it is the most nutritionally-sound diet available because there is no elimination of food categories—only the elimination of "anti-nutrition" or poor nutritional foods. The 20% Indulgence is even more easily assimilated and eliminated from the body due to the cleaning up of the overall system response. If participants are cognizant of balance (which is taught), their nutritional profile should be spot on and result in weight loss (if needed), improved cardiovascular health, improved lipid profiles, and more.

- o Pros: Balance and emotional alignment are at the heart of this Lifestyle Diet. In addition to nutritional balance, participants are taught how to align their emotions for positive hormone support as well.
- o Cons: Active participation is required to achieve all of the benefits. This is not a passive lifestyle diet where an organization does all of the work. Success of this program requires full participation of the participant.

****4 out of 5 Stars

✓ Short-Term Results: "Rapid Results" is one of the eating plans offered, and if this plan is selected, weight loss is one of the many results. The *80/20 Lifestyle Diet* does not operate on a calorie-in versus calorie-out model; instead it opts for quality of nutrition and compliance to the selected eating plan. This approach re-routes nutrition, filling in the nutritional deficits, eliminating superfluous calories, and replacing them with quality nutrition.

- o Pros: By eliminating anti-nutrition (processed foods, additives, preservatives, etc.), participants will begin feeling better on a cellular level within the first two weeks.
- o Cons: Participants must be willing to lean into the discomfort of breaking patterns, reawakening their taste buds, daily journaling and refinement of problem solving skills. This is an active program with no short cuts.

***** 5 out of 5 Stars

✓ Long-Term Results: The *80/20 Lifestyle* was specifically designed to evolve into a "forever," nutritional platform and not a temporary eating plan. As a result, participants change more than their food choices—they change their entire attitude toward nutrition. The *80/20 Lifestyle* is a holistic approach to a healthier approach to positive change in any area of your life through the integration of pillars of support. The long-term outlook for participants of the *80/20 Lifestyle Diet* is bright.

  o Pros: The *80/20 Lifestyle Diet* was created for long-term success.

  o Cons: None.

 *****5 out of 5 Stars

✓ Family Integration: The *80/20 Lifestyle Diet* was created with families in mind. If the nutritional gatekeeper of the home is interested in upgrading their family's nutrition, breaking unwanted eating habits, and introducing a framework that each family member can grow within and take into adulthood, the *80/20 Lifestyle Diet* is the perfect diet.

  o Pros: The *80/20 Lifestyle Diet* was specifically created to reclaim today's processed food obsessed family culture. The *80/20 Lifestyle Diet* provides step-by-step tips for family integration.

  o Cons: Participants must comply with the guidelines and take advantage of the tools offered in order to achieve full family integration.

 *****5 out of 5 Stars

I am not going to tell you which approach is best for you. But what I will tell you is this: whatever weight loss plan you decide to follow and set as your nutrition pillar, you must try to honor the plan in its entirety. When we get into the Four Phases of Transformation, you will see how each pillar provides necessary strength and the overall power of the complete system.

When considering which weight loss, weight management or overall nutritional elevation plan to select, it is helpful if you approach this decision while considering the following questions:

1. Can you see yourself eating this way for the rest of your life?
2. Does this nutrition plan allow you to enjoy social engagements and special time with family and friends?
3. Is the nutritional plan you selected timeless?
4. Is this a nutritional plan that can healthfully nourish all family members?
5. Are there phases or stages of nutrition that allow for flexibility?

6. Finally, can you see yourself eating this way for the rest of your life?

The system I am outlining in this book will work with any nutrition plan (weight loss, weight management, overall nutritional elevation) out there because the focus is not on the diet, but on a holistic approach to making lifestyle changes in a state of joy and inspiration.

For more information, visit BeforetheFork.com and pick up *The 80/20 Lifestyle Diet: A 28-Day Guide to Total Lifestyle Transformation*. This is a step-by-step program that provides a 28-day meal plan, and is the perfect companion to *Before the Fork*.

I used to be a white-knuckle flier! Every time I would board a plane I would say a prayer, bless everyone I knew, and thank God for the wonderful life He had given me and ask Him to please take care of my loved ones because I knew I was going to die! I would grip the armrest, and move between focused, meditative breathing and straight up holding my breath. Each bump, dip, and swerve I felt I was certain we were going down! I even went as far as to cancel several really fun trips because I was gripped with fear and the thought of flying paralyzed me. And then I married my husband Greg... an avid airplane enthusiast and pilot from a long-line of zealous flyers.

I remember our first flight together: I was trying to put on a brave face, but inside I was trembling. Greg knew every detail of the plane, including the make, model and year the airplane was built. He would refer to the plane as the aircraft and use words like "flight-level" when explaining to me how high we would be flying, and "air pocket" to describe turbulence. He spoke the language of flight. Greg could always comfort me on a plane and was sure to put my mind at ease when we flew together. He went on to get his pilot's license and purchase a plane, and to this day enjoys flying for the sheer pleasure of it.

Although I am no longer even the slightest bit afraid of flying, I am still amused by Greg's fascination with flight and my lack of interest. As an enthusiast, Greg enjoys devouring any and all information on flight, and all I need to know is that my aircraft is safe, my pilot is well-trained, and the conditions are favorable for a smooth flight. Regardless of his vast knowledge of flight and my lack of knowledge, we both arrive safely!

What does a fear of flying, knowledge of flying, and fitness have to do with each other? Well, everything! This is a story about two people with two very different perceptions of the same topic. One person extracts great enjoyment and pleasure out of both flying and learning about aircraft, while the other just simply looks at airplanes as transportation from point A to point B. We both ultimately achieve the same goal, but our means of emotional travel are very different.

This observation only led me to more questions in my health and fitness journey: Why do some people perceive fitness as a punishment, while others think of it as a privilege? Why do some people have a "no-pain, no-gain" mentality, while others just want to walk around the block? How can some people exercise at 5:00 am, while others can't pull themselves out of bed? Could the answer be found by simply identifying archetypes? And, within those archetypes, can failure and success be as simple as switching from Red to Green Zone Thinking? The answer is YES!

I began reviewing my past clients and poured over notes of excuses, validations, justifications, rationalizations, and defensiveness. I mapped when these clients made the "shift" from frustration to respect and watched as their love of fitness began to grow and re-shape their lives. This ultimately resulted in the creation of the **Four Archetypes of Fitness**. (Note: There is not a good-better-best archetype hierarchy—only an understanding of each. Identifying which of the four archetypes best describes your disposition is the best way to begin shifting your thinking to support your fitness goals.)

Although the archetypes clearly defined themselves, it ultimately didn't matter which archetypes my clients were. All that mattered was that they made the "shift." When they began to redefine their idea of exercise through Green Zone Thinking and made certain adaptations to their health and fitness interests, a whole new world opened up to them. *Adaptation is the bridge that will carry you from where you are to where you want to go.* The best way to adapt to a moving world is to create and practice your Why Story script, know who you are and where you are going, and stick to your script framed the way it serves you best.

The Four Archetypes of Fitness

An "archetype" is a very typical example of a certain person or thing. Although each of us have different archetypes at play in the many areas that make up our life, it is helpful to know that only four archetypes dominate our relationship with fitness. Recognizing your archetype will give you a new point-of-reference from which you can begin to analyze, disarm and redirect your excuses.

1. **Rebel**
2. **Seeker**
3. **Perfectionist**
4. **Hacker**

1. The Rebel

The Rebel's greatest fear is powerlessness, and as a result they push against expectations, both inner and outer. They possess a wisdom, and awareness, yet their natural defensiveness often ignites their spirit of opposition.

At their best, Rebels are authentic, free-spirited, and determined. At their worst, Rebels are oppositional, resistant, defensive.

What a Rebel needs to know:

"I've always loved the idea of not being what people expect me to be."
~ Rebel Quote

Rebels value independent thinking and tend to resist habits that limit freedom of choice.

- **Be Original**: You crave originality. You may identify better with a fringe sport or activity rather than a mainstream activity. Or if you choose to participate in a main stream activity, do it in a radically different and uniquely YOU way.
- **Frame for Freedom**: You crave freedom. You resent anything or anyone telling you what to do, so frame your fitness with freedom and choice in mind.
- **Disrupt, Destroy, or Shock**: You crave a revolution. You want to shake things up, so disrupt the status quo, destroy the rules, and shock everyone watching.

Rebels are outrageous, radical, and free. You are the wild men and women of the world and all change starts with YOU. Embrace your inner misfit and learn to frame your world for your ultimate success.

You might be a Rebel if...

- You find yourself fighting against expectations from others.
- You prefer being independent and would rather give the orders than take the orders.
- You get annoyed with conformity.
- You stick to your convictions and are prepared to live and die alone rather than compromise your freedom to think for yourself.

The H.A.P.P.I.N.E.S.S. Ladder and Rebels

Hey Rebel, where did you find yourself on the H.A.P.P.I.N.E.S.S. Ladder? If you hovered around the bottom of the ladder in the Red and Yellow Zone, you may already be experiencing the Rebel struggle. The Red and Yellow Zone cultivate the worst of Rebel tendencies.

As a **Red or Yellow Zone Rebel,** you have an innate need to challenge authority (regardless of the consequence), an unwillingness to find middle ground with people that don't think as you do, and your need to push against "life" in general only increases your hardcore Rebel stance. This internal environment robs you of opportunities to reach your personal best.

As a **Green Zone Rebel,** you have everything it takes to effect massive change in your life, and in the world, should you choose to do so. Green Zone Rebels harness the power and energy of high vibration thoughts and use this energy to move mountains. Green Zone Rebels explore and lead others; they are exciting and colorful to be around, enthusiastic and brave. In the face of overwhelming obstacles, Green Zone Rebels show courage. Green Zone Rebels change the world!

Green Zone Rebel Four POWER Words:
Empowered, Independent, Passionate, Determined

H.A.P.P.I.N.E.S.S. Evolution: Rebel

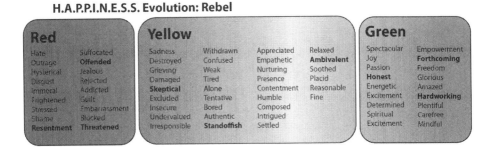

Red		Yellow				Green	
Hate	Suffocated	Sadness	Withdrawn	Appreciated	Relaxed	Spectacular	Empowerment
Outrage	Offended	Destroyed	Confused	Empathetic	Ambivalent	Joy	Forthcoming
Hysterical	Jealous	Grieving	Weak	Nurturing	Soothed	Passion	Freedom
Disgust	Rejected	Damaged	Tired	Presence	Placid	Honest	Glorious
Immoral	Addicted	Skeptical	Alone	Contentment	Reasonable	Energetic	Amazed
Frightened	Guilt	Excluded	Tentative	Humble	Fine	Excitement	Hardworking
Stressed	Embarrassment	Insecure	Bored	Composed		Determined	Plentiful
Shame	Blocked	Undervalued	Authentic	Intrigued		Spiritual	Carefree
Resentment	Threatened	Irresponsible	Standoffish	Settled		Excitement	Mindful

The Story of a Red to Green Zone Rebel: If there is an archetype I am personally familiar with, it would be the Rebel! Not only do I possess a lot of the Rebel characteristics, I was raised by perhaps the most textbook Rebel of all, my dad. As I shared with you earlier, my dad embraced sobriety at the age of thirty-nine after several failed attempts. Something about my dad was different when he left his final alcohol treatment center; he was changed and we all knew it.

His roommate during his stay at this treatment center was a very famous athlete for whom my dad had great admiration and respect. I feel certain my dad made the "shift" because he saw his own struggle in someone he admired so greatly, and this gave my Dad permission to be human. He embraced his vulnerability and began weaving a new story into his life. He let go of years of resentment, anger, defiance, fear and stubbornness, and this release is what allowed him to be "reborn." Dad committed fully to his new life, and began navigating from Green Zone Thinking. This is how he successfully broke the pattern of alcohol abuse and left the numbing effects behind.

Addiction was no longer the *result* of his life — addiction was the *catalyst* for his life and recovery became his greatest gift. Part of my Dad's transformation included redefining his life. He had a clean slate, so what was he going to write on it? At age 39, my dad decided to reclaim his inner athlete. In high school and college, he was a very decorated athlete, and he slowly began his quest to reclaim his fitness that years of alcohol abuse had taken from him.

Racquetball, weights, running, and golf became his new healthy addiction. Through these outlets, my dad has ministered to many in need of transformation. As a Rebel, he has a take-me-at-face-value attitude toward life. What this meant as an active alcoholic living from Red Zone Thinking was, "I'm going to do what I want to do, when I want to do it, and damn the consequences." As a recovering alcoholic perceiving sobriety as a gift and using Green Zone Thinking to navigate life, it now means. "My recovery is my badge, and I wear my badge with honor."

Fitness became such a huge part of my father's life that he wanted to pay it forward. He hired my sons, nieces, and nephews their first personal trainer, and built a gym for his employees. Now, at age seventy-two, he never misses a 5:00 a.m. workout session. Dad's the same guy with the same obsessive-compulsive personality, but he is now operating his life from Green Zone Thinking!

Advice from Robin: *Get on with ya bad self...* Be a rebel! Just learn to use your Rebel energy in a productive Rebel way. Here are a few tips:

- **Be Original:** You are atypical; don't be afraid to try things that are out-of-the-box. You may identify better with a fringe sport or activity rather than a mainstream one.
- **Frame for Freedom:** Rebels crave freedom and resent anything that tells them what to do, so frame your exercise with freedom and choice in mind.
- **You Aren't the Boss of Me:** Rebels often have a cruel "inner dictator." Once a Rebel learns to silence their cruel dictator, they are often led to complete lifestyle transformations.

2. The Seeker

The Seeker strives to be unafraid. The idea of committing to one person, one place, one thing, and even one style for too long can feel claustrophobic. Seekers crave constant self-discovery, but can get lost in the vastness of it all, fearing above all else getting trapped into conformity. This fear and avoidance of conformity can leave them wandering aimlessly.

At their best Seekers are ambitious, self-determined, and loyal to their heart. At their worst they are resentful, non-committal, and flighty.

What a Seeker needs to know:

"Into the wild I go: losing my way, finding my soul." ~Unknown
Grab your Birkenstocks and embrace your inner wonderer! Here are a few tips to help you enjoy the journey.

Seekers value being the brave wanderer and the soul explorer.

- **Engage**: You crave exploring. Don't mistake *exploring different ideas* for avoidance. Chose an activity and engage. Not all journeys are physical, and Seekers can get lost in ideas void of execution.
- **Embrace Freedom**: You crave freedom. Seekers tend to be restless, so allow your fitness to move between indoor and outdoor, never relying on one source to meet all your needs. Variety and flexibility will breathe a sense of adventure into your fitness.
- **"Light" Your Way**: You crave enlightenment and connection. You are always on a journey, whether internal or external; try incorporating spirituality into your fitness for a more fulfilling experience.

Seekers have the stories because they dare to live where others only dream. You are the gypsies of the world and you bring beauty, inquisitiveness, and flavor to all you do. Don't fight your need to explore; embrace it and incorporate it!

You might be a Seeker if...

- You crave freedom to explore your thoughts.
- You want deeper, more meaningful experiences.
- You fear being trapped in a meaningless life.

- You find yourself wandering aimlessly without a sense of direction or purpose.
- Your desires are vague and undefined.

The H.A.P.P.I.N.E.S.S. Ladder and Seekers

Where did you find yourself on the H.A.P.P.I.N.E.S.S. Ladder? If you are a Red or Yellow Zone Seeker, you may be experiencing the frustration of feeling lost and overwhelmed. Red and Yellow Zone thinking renders the Seeker stuck, overwhelmed, limited and even hopeless.

As a **Red or Yellow Zone Seeker**, you frame your life as limited and constricting. You wander aimlessly and without purpose simply because your clarity is impaired by your feelings of overwhelm. Your need to explore as experienced through Red and Yellow Zone thinking robs you of the present experience.

As a **Green Zone Seeker,** you are the person who spreads joy and happiness everywhere you go. Green Zone Seekers reframe every area of their life for pleasure. They don't just make a cup of coffee in the morning; they create extravagant creamy "coffee-like" beverages worthy of a spot on any coffee shop menu. They even find the journey in navigating the darkest situations. Green Zone Seekers find wonder in every experience. They inspire most everyone they meet to embrace life on a higher level and find joy in the journey.

Green Zone Seeker Four POWER Words:
Freedom, Variety, Flexibility, Passion

H.A.P.P.I.N.E.S.S. Evolution: Seeker

Red		Yellow				Green	
Hate	Confused	Sadness	Withdrawn	Empathetic	Relaxed	Spectacular	Empowerment
Outrage	Suffocated	Destroyed	Confused	Flaky	Soothed	Joy	Freedom
Hysterical	Jealous	Grieving	Weak	Nurturing	Placid	Passion	Glorious
Disgust	Rejected	Damaged	Tired	Presence	Reasonable	Energetic	Interested
Trapped	Addicted	Excluded	Alone	Contentment	Over-	Excitement	Amazed
immoral	Guilt	Restless	Tentative	Humble	whelmed	Curious	Plentiful
Frightened	Embarrassment	Insecure	Bored	Composed	Fine	Determined	Carefree
Stressed	Blocked	Undervalued	Authentic	Intrigued		Spiritual	Open
Shame	Discontent	Irresponsible	Appreciated	Settled		Excitement	Mindful

The Story of a Red to Green Zone Seeker: If you can name your close friends on more than one hand, consider yourself very fortunate. You may have 2,000 friends on various forms of social media, but how many *Heart Space* friends do you have? Heart Space friends are those who blur the line of family and move into a space in your heart reserved for only the most unconditional love. I have one of those friends, and I treasure her beyond words. Her "BIG" story is what novels are made of...

Kelly and I have been doing life together since the age of eight. We rode our bikes to elementary school, we did sleepovers and birthday parties, we drove together in her Jeep Scrambler or my Fiat Spyder in high school, and we were as close as two people can be. I was super-shy and Kelly was an amazing front man. Her energy and life force is off the charts and her laugh is infectious. After high school, we spent ages eighteen to twenty-one apart as we both learned to navigate the world of "adulting." By the time we were twenty-two, we were back on track as each other's "safe space." We both married and had our first babies only two months apart. Here is where the plot twist begins...

Kelly is an incredibly intelligent girl. She may be all laughter and party games on the outside, but on the inside, she has many complex layers. At the young age of twenty-six, she became the sole provider for her daughter. Kelly had a good job and worked her way up the ranks from mailroom to president. She felt it a privilege to be able to provide a life for her daughter that was rich in love, discipline, freedom, and choice. Kelly chose to live a comfortable, yet frugal life.

While making her way up the ladder of Corporate America her salary grew, yet her lifestyle never changed. During the 25+ years Kelly dedicated to raising her daughter, growing her business and nurturing the daughter, sister, and friend relationships in her life, she knew she was denying a yearning inside herself. She filled the yearning with a variety fitness classes, small get-a-ways, decorating, a little shopping, but nevertheless there was a hole that was just growing wider and deeper.

As fate would have it, her life unexpectedly opened up several years ago, and Kelly sold her business and walked away from Corporate America. For the first time in her life she had the opportunity to explore that yearning that had been her constant companion for years. Come to find out, Kelly is a Seeker. Her life had previously left little room to discover the Seeker that lived inside. Once her world opened up and she gained the freedom to move about in her new life, she came to recognize her yearning as her messenger. Kelly is so grateful for her time in Corporate America. She recognizes that it afforded her a lifestyle that cared for her daughter generously and has allowed her to retire at 50 years young. But she also acknowledges the imbalance required to be successful at that level.

Kelly today is a completely different woman than only five short years ago. She's traveled, made many friends along the way, and satisfied her craving for spiritual adventure. Corporate Kelly denied her Seeker for so many years and met struggle with frustration and bits and pieces of panic. The new Seeker Kelly meets struggle with curiosity and a willingness to discover the highest answer. For the first time in a long time, I feel the world is getting to enjoy the girl I have called my best friend for over forty-three years.

One final note on Kelly's wonderful transformation: Corporate Kelly paid thousands of dollars hiring personal trainers and exploring expensive fitness classes. She would ebb and flow between her love and hate of the process. Weight loss always stayed just out of her reach as she navigated the stressful corporate world. Flash forward to Seeker Kelly, and within six months of leaving behind corporate life, she stumbled upon her physical passions: walking and yoga. She doesn't push her body outside of its comfort zone, she doesn't count calories, she doesn't stress over how many times she's exercised in a week — she just walks and has a gentle practice of yoga. During a recent trip to Mexico, Kelly spent her time peacefully strolling the streets, meeting people, buying fresh juices and enjoying a street taco before walking back to her casa. Guess what? She lost thirty pounds!

Kelly allowed herself to reframe her thinking. She became radically illogical. She invited adventure into her life, threw away her watch, trusted her gut, and took a trust fall into her new life. She didn't discover beaches and sunshine –she discovered happiness! Her weight loss, health and overall glow is a direct result of her aligning with what truly brings her joy and that is loving people, discovering new passions, navigating new emotions, being exactly who she is at that moment and allowing others to be the same.

I know we all can't leave behind our lives for a life of carefree travel. But realizing you are a Seeker may allow you to reframe your world and start inviting the Seeker in you to take part in your life. Carve out a niche in your life that serves the Seeker.

Advice from Robin: *Follow your soul...* it knows the way! Here are a few tips:

- Seekers tend to be restless, so allow your fitness freedom. Move between indoor fitness and outdoor fitness never relying on one source to meet all your needs.
- Seekers crave a spiritual connection, so try incorporating spirituality into your fitness for a more fulfilling experience.
- Seekers want to be enlightened and are always on a journey whether internal or external. Explore a variety of fitness styles and embrace your never-ending quest.

3. The Perfectionist

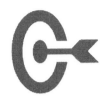

The Perfectionist values perception above all else. They rarely take into account the amount of effort, emotional toll, or sacrifice required to complete a task; as a result people's feelings are rarely considered. A Perfectionist often signs up for ambitious goals as a way of highlighting their perfectionism.

At their best, Perfectionists are accomplished leaders, daring and focused. At their worst, they are unable to delegate, unreasonable, critical, and unforgiving.

What a Perfectionist needs to know:

"I will hold myself to a standard of grace, not perfection." ~Unknown

Perfectionism is not about healthy striving; it is a protective shield worn to avoid judgment. If a Perfectionist feels too vulnerable or ill-equipped to master a skill, they tend to abandon the activity all together. "Failure to launch" is a struggle shared by Perfectionists. Here are a few tips to reframe your perfectionist tendencies around fitness.

- **Get Started:** Allow yourself to be a beginner.
- **You vs. You:** Perfectionists are self-critical, often judging their own accomplishments against the accomplishments of others. Focus on your accomplishments, appreciate how far you have come, and do not compare yourself to others.
- **Be Nice:** Green Zone Self-talk is extremely important to a perfectionist. Create a soothing internal dialog to comfort feelings of discontent, inadequacy and harsh self-judgment. Speak to yourself the way you would speak to someone you treasure.

The most destructive aspect of being a Perfectionist is the judgment you place on yourself and the value you place on others opinion of you. Embrace your inner Perfectionist, but beware of the emotional battle. You will thrive best with a day-by-day approach and adopting the mantra "Find Joy in the Journey." Switch your focus from excellence to progress!

You might be a Perfectionist if...

- You have trouble completing tasks because you think there is always

more that could be done to improve the project.
- Your sense of accomplishment is affected by how others react to you.
- You avoid situations where you think you might not excel.
- You are either all-in or nothing-at-all.

The H.A.P.P.I.N.E.S.S. Ladder and Perfectionists

The Perfectionist's Plight: Where did you find yourself on the H.A.P.P.I.N.E.S.S. Ladder? I can assure you that Red and Yellow Zone Perfectionists are deeply frustrated individuals. If you are a Red and/or Yellow Zone Perfectionist, even your happiest moments are denied their full joy.

As a **Red or Yellow Zone Perfectionist,** you are in constant competition with a fictitious standard. This fictitious standard may be the result of a seed planted through a variety of facilitators: society, schools, parenting, religion, even the media. You struggle with an all-or-nothing mentality, denying yourself the opportunity of being a beginner simply because you feel you should begin as an expert. You demand perfection in yourself as well as others. You are emotionally overworked, spiritually drained, and you never feel as if you measure up.

As a **Green Zone Perfectionist,** you have turned your Red and Yellow Zone emotions upside down. You no longer strive for perfection; you strive for progress. Couple this slight shift in perspective with your natural sense of responsibility, innate leadership skills and inner drive and you have all the makings of a game changer. Green Zone Perfectionists (or should we say, Green Zone Recovering Perfectionists) are vertical thinkers, great organizers, have an eye for detail, and are brilliantly analytical. So don't lose sight of the big picture instead, realize "finished" is better than perfect." Embrace flexibility and not only will you will fall in love with the journey, you will be on the path of great achievement (for the right reasons).

The Story of a Red to Green Zone Perfectionist: I absolutely love living in a small town! The intimacy, sense of family, community support, and familiarity is very comforting to me. I have a personal relationship with my dry cleaner, banker, pharmacist, and many store clerks. But I have a special relationship with the people inside my grocery store. We talk food passionately every time I shop, and I love it. One day several years ago, I dropped by the grocery store to grab a few things for dinner. I made my way down an aisle where a young girl I had known for years was crouched down picking up large jars of beans and stocking the shelves; her name was Heather.

Heather went to school with two of my boys. She was a very accomplished student, a pageant competitor, president of student council, and an employee of the grocery store. We made eye contact and Heather briefly stopped to give me a hug and she went right back to squatting and stacking the heavy containers filled with beans.She was reaching, stretching and placing heavy cans way over her head. Prior to grocery shopping I had taught a class at my gym, so I still had my workout clothes on, hair in a ponytail, and reeked of sweat. My appearance must have sparked the following conversation.

"Between work, school, student counsel, and prom committee, I have no time to exercise. I really wish I could go to the gym and workout, but life is crazy," Heather said with a sigh. She had gained several pounds since the last time I saw her, and I could sense how uncomfortable she was with her expanding size. Heather went on to talk about the difficulty she was having in balancing her schedule.

I smiled, took her hand in mine and said, "Heather, what do you call what you are doing now?" She looked at me wide-eyed and puzzled, and she had no idea what I was talking about. I went on to explain to her that her lifting and squatting, reaching, stretching and twisting was exercise. I told her to squat down and not bend over, gave her basic lifting advice to minimize injury, and told her to embrace her very physical job as her exercise.I said, "Perform your job with enthusiasm and vigor. Move quickly, purposefully with the intent of burning calories." I suggested she use her mobile device and track her calorie burn while working. Then I dropped the bombshell that changed her thinking...I gave her my number and later on a call together we developed her 80/20 eating plan.

Heather didn't need to exercise any more: her job was exercise, she just didn't recognize it! Once she aligned her thinking, and added 80/20 nutrition, her extra pounds fell off. She was a perfectionist so I knew she would need to measure her results, but it was her shift that allowed her to move into Green Zone Thinking and redefine her world in the way a perfectionist must redefine their world.

Here are a few tips:

- **Focus on getting started and embrace evolution:** As humans we evolve daily, so don't deny yourself the opportunity of being a beginner simply out of fear of not being perfect.

- **JUST STOP IT:** To a great degree, Perfectionism is a result of constant Red Zone Thinking. Perfectionists are self-critical and often struggle with feelings of inadequacy that form negative thought patterns. Your internal dialog is a nagging reflection of emotional toxicity. When you learn to navigate the H.A.P.P.I.N.E.S.S. Ladder, much of your undesirable behavior will correct itself.

- **Be Nice:** Green Zone Self-talk is extremely important to a perfectionist. Create a soothing internal dialog to comfort feelings of discontent, inadequacy and harsh self-judgment. Speak to yourself the way you would speak to someone you treasure.

4. The Hacker

The Hacker values competence above all else. Hackers crave an experience-based environment that allows them to play with ideas, theories, and outcomes, all in an effort to achieve knowledge. Hackers think outside the box, creatively, scientifically and futuristically. They back away from accepting opinions, preferring to test ideas for themselves. It may take years, even decades, for their contribution to be acknowledged, validated and integrated into everyday life, but you can be certain that the world benefits from these visionary pioneers.

At their best, Hackers are intuitive, innovative, daring, independent thinkers. At their worst, they are know-it-alls, overly-complicated, condescending, and avoidant.

What a Hacker needs to know:

"They said don't give up on your dreams, so I went back to sleep." ~Unknown

Hackers build their identity around "ideas" and can easily become lost in their research. Hackers strive to cultivate a level of expertise around certain subjects that are typically "off the grid" or "fringe" ideas. Hackers will benefit from learning to act on limited information, rather than hoarding information in an attempt to quench their unquenchable appetite for knowledge.

If your natural tendency is to explore uncharted water... don't stay stuck in discovery. Here are some tips to move you forward.

- **Teach:** That's right, teach what you know. You have brilliant observation skills, and you notice more than the average person, so put your skills to use and teach. At least you will be paying your knowledge forward even if you long to dive even deeper into the research!
- **Analyze:** It's part of your nature, so put it to good use. 30/70 split! In-

vest 30% of your time contemplating the problem and 70% on creating problem-solving tools. Because you are a fantastic analyst you give great advice, therefore when you assume a leadership role you have the knowledge, instincts, and ability to back it up!

- **Forecast:** You have the gift of strong intuition, so use it. Hackers are always gathering information whether they are aware of it or not. This often is reflected in their intuitive ability to predict the future. They see patterns and are able to predict outcomes. Use this to your advantage when planning your workouts or setting goals. Become your own experiment.

You might be a Hacker if...
- You dwell and thrive on investigating fringe ideas.
- You denounce mainstream ideas in search of drawing your own conclusion.
- You have to learn the intricacies of an idea, concept, or system thoroughly.
- When making decisions you invest countless hours researching which can lead to analysis-paralysis.
- You constantly seek to understand the world and the people in it.
- You are a committed life-long learner.

The H.A.P.P.I.N.E.S.S. Ladder and Hackers

Hacking or Hiding? Hey Hacker, where did you find yourself on the H.A.P.P.I.N.E.S.S. Ladder? You are a brilliant researcher, but if you are spending too much time in Red and Yellow Zone thinking, your insecurities are getting the best of you.

As a **Red or Yellow Zone Hacker,** you are filled with deep insecurities and struggle with the idea of "measuring up." You invest countless hours of research, pouring over data, forming hypothesis on one specific topic just in order to avoid engagement in other areas of life you feel less equipped to do as well as others. You escape into your mind where you feel most capable. An imbalanced Hacker often ignores interpersonal relationships and other important areas of life due to their hyper-focused nature. Extreme Red Zone Thinking leads a Hacker to withdraw and become reclusive, eccentric and highly unstable. Yellow Zone Hackers are a little less desperate but nonetheless ineffective. They spend most of their time fine-tuning ideas and very little time acting on those ideas.

As a **Green Zone Hacker,** your mind will lead you to great discoveries and innovations. You are a visionary, pioneering discoveries in an entirely new way. Artfully balancing your need to acquire mastery of any subject that interests you with the benefits of developing strong interpersonal skills. Green Zone Hackers are remarkable in their ability to grasp broad concepts and find entirely new ways of perceiving things. Their mental capacity can be an extraordinary gift when lived from Green Zone Thinking, but when influenced by Red and Yellow Zone Thinking, Hackers can become nervous and high-strung. So find healthy ways to relax such as, meditation, jogging, and yoga. Pick subjects to fixate on that serve your personal growth because your mind is a fertile playground be selective of the seeds you sow. Finally, try not to get lost in thinking and speculating outside of designated research time; bring your thoughts back to the now for a deeper more meaningful life experience.

Green Zone Hacker Four POWER Words:
Relax, Focus, Trust, Notice, Act

H.A.P.P.I.N.E.S.S. Evolution: Hacker

Red		Yellow				Green	
Hate	Eccentric	Sadness	Confused	Empathetic	Settled	Spectacular	Empowerment
Outrage	Suffocated	Destroyed	Weak	Nurturing	Relaxed	Joy	Freedom
Hysterical	Jealous	Grieving	**Fearful**	Presence	Soothed	Passion	Glorious
Disgust	**Reclusive**	Damaged	Tired	Contentment	Placid	**Visionary**	**Creative**
Immoral	Rejected	Excluded	Alone	**Procrasti-nate**	Reasonable	Energetic	Amazed
Neurotic	Addicted	Insecure	Tentative	Humble	**Isolated**	Excitement	Plentiful
Frightened	Guilt	Undervalued	Bored	Composed	Fine	Determined	Carefree
Stressed	Embarrassment	Irresponsible	Authentic	Intrigued		Spiritual	**Innovative**
Shame	Blocked	Withdrawn	Appreciated			Excitement	Mindful

The Story of a Red to Green Zone Hacker:

This book is the direct result of me being a Hacker. I hacked the connection between spirituality, neuroscience, and behavioral science. One thing I have come to understand is that you do not have to be a Hacker to benefit from the time, energy and dedication these pioneers have invested in making your life easier to navigate. I don't know how to build a plane, but I still benefit from the flight. Meal Stacking was my number one mealtime hack, and it was instrumental in getting my family back to the dinner table.

When I train women in my gym, I use a system I created that is efficient, respectful of their time, and very results focused — it is my gym hack. Journaling is my hack for realigning with my goals and setting the tone of my day. Hacks do not have to be complicated contraptions you wear; pills, potions, or lotions you take, or even tanks you float in. If they help you reach your goals more efficiently and with less effort, they are hacks.

In my Facebook feed this morning, a post popped up from 2010: *I am actively developing my lifestyle book. It is my goal to bring you the most com-*

prehensive and thorough plan I possibly can. If you are interested in receiving information upon the book's completion, please private message me and I will add you to my list. What? 2010? What the heck have I been doing all these years? Oh, right, I've been researching! Hackers aren't always time efficient, and we often get lost in our data because the process of discovery is as exciting as the actual discovery. We love our laboratory and the discovery process. There's something about committing our research to print that finalizes it, and that is a hard thing for a Hacker to do. To a Hacker, nothing is ever final — it is only "on hold" until more data is found.

I knew in order to serve people, as I had always intended, I had to figure out a way to "hack" my hacking. This is where I discovered that, like body-types, each person is typically a combination of two, maybe more, archetypes. Take me, for example: I am a dominate Hacker (this is indisputable), but the Seeker in me also enjoyed the process of self-discovery, and completing the book would put an end to my fun. Or, maybe it was the Perfectionist in me that kept delaying the book out of fear of it being imperfect. Either way, I had to be hacked. First, I hired an editor, and her contribution to this project is immeasurable; without her I would still be gathering data and posting my intentions on Facebook. She held me accountable to deadlines, reined me in when my message became unintelligible, and curated my work so it translated well. Second, with the help of my editor, I committed to two additional projects immediately following the completion of this book. This commitment will serve my Seeker, allowing me to sink my teeth into another meaningful project.

The thing about Hackers is this: we go where very few have an interest in going. We love the process, the knowledge, the variety, the discovery, but sometimes our curiosity leaves us stuck in discovery. We all know that person who has all the knowledge about weight loss, exercise, etc., but can't seem to make strides in that area of their life. Here is a quick story that demonstrates an information Hacker who lacks the ability to effect change in their own life.

Several years ago, I was on vacation in Florida and became ill. I knew I needed an antibiotic, so I went to the local walk-in clinic where a nice doctor saw me. He was about seventy pounds overweight, and when he sat next to me, I could smell the cigarette smoke on his clothes. He was so knowledgeable and we had a great conversation about health, weight loss, nutrition, and so on. When I left his office, I realized he was a knowledge Hacker, a walking, talking medical encyclopedia, yet he never acquired the skills to move his vast knowledge into actionable steps to change his own life. He certainly did not lack the knowledge — he lacked the skills.

Advice from Robin: One foot on the dock and one foot on the boat can wind you up in the water! Sometimes what you know at the moment is enough (for the moment); it moves the ball forward! Rather than hoarding information like a dysfunctional cat lady, you must learn that finished is better than perfect and never forget perfect is an illusion. Don't stay stuck in discovery. Here are some tips to move you forward.

- **Teach:** That's right, teach what you know. You have brilliant observational skills; you notice more than the average person, so put your skills to use and teach. At least you will be paying your knowledge forward even if you long to dive even deeper into the research!
- **Analyzing is part of your nature:** As a result, you may spend more time contemplating problems, but you also are more likely to create an entire arsenal of problem-solving tools. Consider your Hacker nature another puzzle to solve and put your focus on creating tools to move you through the research and into action.
- **Forecast through intuition:** Hackers are always gathering information whether they are aware of it or not. This often is reflected in their intuitive ability to predict the future. They see patterns and are able to predict outcomes. Use this to your advantage when planning your workouts and setting goals. Become your own experiment!

Free-Form Fitness and the Four Archetypes of Fitness

Physical fitness is achieving a general state of good health, most often as a result of exercise and good nutrition. Such a simple definition, yet something the majority of us struggle to execute for a lifetime.

Free-Form Fitness is the philosophy of allowing any and all forms of movement — regardless of the intensity, variety, and specificity — to move freely throughout one's life with the singular purpose of enhanced quality of living.

This means it will look differently to a 22-year-old male than it will for a 45-year-old female. The idea with Free-Form Fitness is allowance. Allowing yourself the freedom to accept or reject fitness trends, and allowing the right to move between disciplines in an effort to find the best fit for you personally at that particular time in your life. Free-Form Fitness is ever-moving, ever-changing, ever-evolving. It is not delaying fitness, rather it is embracing movement in all its forms and never defining your fitness through one singular activity.

Free-Form Fitness broadens public perception of fitness in an effort to make fitness accessible to everyone, athletes, former athletes, non-athletes, young, old, and in between. Fitness can, and should, be incorporated into your life, yet many people deny themselves fitness because they simply do not align with popular fitness trends. They don't consider themselves an athlete, or they played a sport but never fell in love with fitness. Your fitness can be as traditional or as non-traditional as you choose. Free-Form Fitness means you decided how to use your body to achieve your goals. Expose yourself to a variety of ideas and classes. Ride a bike, kayak a river, hike a path, go rock climbing, take a martial arts class, stretch, move and bend in ways you never imagined... or simply lace up your shoes and head out the door!

The Four Archetypes of Fitness were created to inspire each personality to align with fitness from the point of view that will serve them best. Free-Form Fitness introduces fitness from outside of the stereotypical one-size-fits-all, no-pain-no-gain mentality demonstrated on social media and television programming. This combination invites a much larger audience into the fitness discussion.

If you are like me, you recognize parts of yourself in each archetype. I developed the archetypes to help you identify with your natural tendencies so you can create tools that lean into your strengths and protect you from weaknesses. The actual archetype you most identify with is less important than understanding how to communicate with yourself; what motivates you, what de-motivates you, how to frame situations, questions, and even ideas. There is no hierarchy of archetypes, no one personality is better than another — the idea is to identify the best way to move yourself into action from Green Zone Thinking. Knowing your archetype allows you to communicate better with yourself in an effort to move you into action from a position of positive mental energy.

I hope this chapter has inspired you to think a little differently about fitness. The Tips, Tools and Techniques section of the book is full of helpful ideas to support habit change. Your job is to equip your toolbox with appropriate tools that work for you. It's not about anyone else, just you!

Chapter Eleven
Pillar Five: Support

When I made the conscious decision to take my life back, reclaim my family's dinner table, stop dieting, and to create a life that was steeped deeply in respect and gratitude, I intuitively knew I was going to have to go it alone. In God's brilliance, however, he prepared my heart for this journey. Even though I had the love of my four little boys and my husband who adored me, I was the leader of this particular journey.

I am so grateful that God prepared my heart that day. Otherwise, the obstacles I faced would've been too great. When I say God prepared my heart, what I mean by that is I didn't look for support in areas that it did not exist. But beyond that, I had no resentment for the lack of support. God had prepared me with a gentle knowing and a patient heart and a sense of responsibility to assume a leadership role in this area of my family's life. *Does that make sense to you?*

In other words, my husband and my children were not equipped to provide support in an area that they both lacked interest and incentive. Rather than becoming resentful of the additional challenges that added, I included the challenges and incorporated the problem-solving skills into the whole matrix. Their moments of defiance, frustration with me, lack of support, their little sabotaging manipulative attempts at derailing me or us as a family only added to my delight as I wrapped up additional strategies and just kept on track. I released them from the responsibility of being my support team, and I found the support I needed elsewhere. As my journey continued, they began to join me. Now they are the source of some of my greatest support.

Two years ago, after several months of an intense work schedule, I retreated into my sanctuary of books. I had been spending twelve plus hours a day pouring myself into my clients and their needs, and when my schedule opened up, I found myself not even wanting to speak with anyone. I just wanted to curl up with a good book and get lost in a story. One day, I was feeling a little guilty about disengaging from life and I mentioned it to Mac, who I treasure as a trusted advisor in my life. He looked at me and without missing a beat, mincing words or trying to over-analyze me, he simply said, "There is a time to work out and a time to work-in. You are working-in right now Mom, nothing wrong with that!" What a liberating point of view! So, I stopped feeling guilty about my respite of quiet reflection and took the time I needed for self-care.

Your search for support may begin with your retreat from everything. Sometimes you must slow down the momentum of your current life before you can begin momentum in a new direction. Your very first step might be as simple as allowing yourself to retreat into the quiet space in your mind, empty out the old, and begin filling yourself up again with the new. This can be achieved through reading, live events, videos, podcasts, etc. The goal is to quiet the noise of the old you and immerse yourself in the new world you are craving to become part of. Once you have allowed yourself the time of quiet contemplation and support, you are ready for your Public Proclamation. An effective support system consists of three things:

1. Safe - You must feel safe within your support system. It must be an environment free of judgment. It also must be an environment that you feel comfortable sharing.

2. Empathetic - Your support system must understand your struggle, and that is only possible through a shared experience. Empathy requires emotional identification with another person's struggle.

3. Solution-focused - Your support system must be solution-focused and not problem focused. Support conversations should always be rooted in solutions (tips, tools, and techniques) that support a future outcome, rather than getting stuck discussing the problems with no forward plan.

How do I support others? I have a **Three Strike Rule** when it comes to support with my one-on-one clients. That may sound very harsh to some of you, but it serves my clients, and that is all I care about. Here's my rule: Bring me a problem once and I will lean into that problem with you in the most loving and empathetic way that I know how. We will identify the problem by spending the time necessary to uncover the struggle (typically no more than fifteen minutes). Next, we will create a tool or multiple tools to eliminate, redirect, or be better prepared. At the end, we bless the problem for allowing us the opportunity to grow. This is the first strike.

Bring me the same problem a second time, and I will invest half the time, only discussing the tools that we have already identified. We will walk through the missteps, and we will refine the use of the tools. This is the second strike.

Before the Fork

If you bring same problem a third time and it will garner none of my attention, for this reason. Continuing to discuss your problem when it is clear that you're not prepared to implement the tools moves me, as your counselor, from problem-solving facilitator, which is a Creation role in your life, to a problem-reinforcing enabler, which is a Survival role in your life.

My role changes from someone helping them *build their dream* to someone contributing to the reasons *why their dream cannot be built.* Although my lack of engagement sometimes frustrates my clients when they reach their third strike, they understand this is how I operate. I bless them and remind them that they are welcome to come back when they are prepared to focus on Creation. Until then, I am contributing to their limitedness, and I love them entirely too much to do that. I can't begin to tell you how many have returned, acknowledging their responsibility for staying stuck in their limited beliefs. We readjust and we push through. Your support system has to be that bold. The people you seek out for support have to be so committed to your success that they are willing to hit you right between the eyes with the truth. Support will follow a natural progression that organically falls into three categories:

1. Quiet Contemplation: Before your Public Proclamation, it is important to spend time in Quiet Contemplation. This time allows you to fill yourself with new ideas, possibilities, and prepares you to embrace the uncertainty of change. Just buying this book is an act of quiet contemplation. You are thinking about ways to embrace change and you are introducing new thoughts and ideas. In addition to books, podcasts, videos, etc., it would also be wise to begin your journaling now. As soon as you cross over from Quiet Contemplation to Public Proclamation, the naysayers will come calling, the doubt will start screaming in your head, and you will want to run home to what is familiar. If you prepare yourself during your Quiet Contemplation with reasons why you want to change, you can resist the naysayers, the doubt, and even the safe harbor of familiar. When you are ready to share your new intentions with family and friends, attend a public event, or sign up for that exercise class,you are moving into your next stage: Public Proclamation.

Side note: I highly advise you to protect your intentions. Only share your hopes, goals, and dreams with the most supportive people in your life (that may not turn out to be the people you think it may be.) It may be people once removed from your life that share your struggle. My point is: be selective and protect your intentions. You are only one negative comment away from running back to familiar. Now is not the time to overcome these negative people; your silence is golden. Even if they are trying to protect you, you must first protect yourself and guard your dreams.

2. Public Proclamation: You guarded your dreams from naysayers and allowed your hopes to take root. Once you feel adequately nourished through Quiet Contemplation, you will take the biggest leap of all, Public Proclamation. This is where you will find your tribe! During your Quiet Contemplation, you gained strength and your public proclamation is a coming-out party of sorts! You are ready to share your intentions publicly. By the end of the Public Proclamation phase, your transformation will be undeniable. Your public proclamation is where you find your tribe, practice, lean into the discomfort of change, listen to others, support others, and be supported. Those naysayers you protected yourself from will be wondering what the heck has happened in your life. They may become the first group of people that come asking for your help with their own journey.

3. Pay-it-Forward: The final phase of support is to pay-it-forward. Once you take someone by the hand, become their tribe, and pour all of your knowledge into them, you have honored the process. In honoring the process, you are completing the circle of support. Paying it forward also reinforces everything you have just experienced. Because, like it or not, we are human and familiar will always be there with the temptation of running home to the way life used to be. This is why support is a never-ending circle. You are always moving within this circle — sometimes getting, sometimes giving, but always participating.

Don't leave support to chance. Be intentional, recognize the phases, and be an active participant in building your invaluable network of support. Beware of the naysayers and protect yourself, and know that familiar will be a loud voice calling you home where life is predictable. Spend as much time as necessary moving from Quiet Contemplation to Public Proclamation and be willing to go back into Quiet Contemplation when you need self-care. Finally, if you stumble into a support system that is not serving you, do not be afraid to move on and find another tribe. Sometimes you must let go of what is to make room for what is coming. A support system will not "save you," but they will be by your side as you learn to "save yourself."

Before the Fork

Chapter Twelve
Pillar Six: Setting Your Expectations & Custom Goal Setting

Expectations are a strong belief that something will happen in the future. The key word here is belief. To help this make more sense, let's dive a little deeper into the psychology of expectations. We each have two sets of expectations, **Internal Expectations**, which are our beliefs, and **External Expectations**, which are our desires. When we desire what we believe is possible, there is little to stand in our way of achieving our dreams. But when our desire is not supported by our belief, we unconsciously sabotage ourselves. This internal/external system is not easily felt, but with careful examination, it can be navigated with great success.

There are a few things to consider when setting expectations. What is your belief? What is your desire? Do they match? And what role does admiration play in setting your personal expectation?

In addition to understanding your Internal (beliefs) and External (desires) Expectations, you must also be aware of the role admiration plays in sabotaging your success. Unexamined expectations originating through the distorted lens of admiration can (and often does) lead to heartache, frustration and feelings of failure. Admiration alone is not a strong enough foundation for setting personal expectations because there is much more to be considered. If you have failed repeatedly in your attempt to lose weight and get fit, you must know that you are not failing—you are actually succeeding in meeting your Internal Expectations (beliefs). This is why examination, alignment, and discernment are so important.

First, let's take a look at admiration. Admiration is often a fraud. We find ourselves attracted to a certain shape, style or size without personal consideration. Our admiration often morphs from innocent appreciation of something to be admired, into a new gold standard of "being." Often these fraudulent standards are nothing more than cultural memes fed to us through media. In other words, we begin judging ourselves against a cultural meme that is out of alignment with our Internal Expectation. Did you know that your Internal Expectation is responsible for over 80% of your behavior? Therefore, if your desires (external) and beliefs (internal) are at odds, guess who wins? Your beliefs, every time!

Think back to my *Charlie's Angels* days... I set external expectations based on admiration, I let my admiration turn into my desire, and my desire never consulted with my beliefs. A cultural meme set my new gold standard. Because my beliefs and my desires were not in alignment, I spent years struggling to build a healthy relationship with my body. Where and why we pick up our beliefs is something we will discuss in a moment, but for now the takeaway from admiration is this: there is no standard, and judging ourselves against anyone else is the worst way to set expectations. Appreciate beauty for what it is and stop using it as your measuring stick.

We have all heard the saying, "Comparison is the thief of joy." It is my opinion that comparison alone is not the thief of joy; comparison only robs you of your joy when you compare yourself to another and then attach toxic judgment to your findings. That type of comparison will destroy joy. Healthy comparison feels like innocent observation, it helps us gather information, and boosts motivation. Toxic comparison feels competition and either evokes a sense of superiority or inferiority. Either way, someone loses... ultimately, you.

Admiration that grows into comparison will result in one of two outcomes:
1. **Healthy Comparison** uses a model to inspire effort toward becoming the best version of you.
2. **Toxic Comparison** uses a model as the only standard, and anything short of that standard is failure.

To understand admiration is to understand the birthplace of all desire. It is the stepping stone that can either root you in healthy growth or destroy your chances of growing at all. It can be your Svengali and seduce, dominate, and exploit you, or it can be your teacher and open doors, illuminate the path and support your growth. As this chapter unfolds, you will learn how to embrace admiration and use it as fuel to drive you forward. This skill will empower you by aligning your beliefs with your desires, which is the key to setting effective expectations.

Next, let's take a look at desire. Desire is a moving force in creation. Without a continuous flow of desire, there would no longer be any reason to do anything. Not only is desire necessary to keep us moving forward, it is unquenchable. Once a desire for something is met, another desire takes its place. Advertisers exploit this process through the creation of cultural memes, which we touched on earlier while discussing admiration. These memes begin embedding themselves into our ego mind, which creates a world of disorder if these ideas do not harmonize with our internal belief system. Hinduism, Christianity, and Buddhism all condemn desire as the common destroyer of self-realization. However, we are human and desire is a human emotion — so, what do we do?

We need to learn to acknowledge our desire and place a beautiful frame around it, and hang it in the corners of our mind where it can be appreciated for what it is... but, what exactly is it? It is an idea that awoke in you: a stirring, a feeling, and a discomfort that is asking you to grow. Left unexamined, desire can become toxic and lead to a lifetime of Red Zone Thinking around the subject. If you match your desires with your belief system, not only will you be inspired, you will have the winning formula for meeting and exceeding your expectations!

Finally, let's look at the most complicated player in the game of expectations, your beliefs! To be clear, we are talking about beliefs and not values—and there is a great deal of difference between the two. Your values are universally based on what is important to you, free of the need to judge against past references for context. On the other side, beliefs use past experiences to create assumptions that will apply to all future situations. From an evolutionary perspective, this rapid-fire belief forming system may have been an efficient way to meet our survival need. But, in our complex, continually expanding modern world this is anything but progressive, efficient or conducive to personal growth. Here are a few examples of how a series of simple, events can lead to the formation of disempowering, limiting beliefs:

Example One: A shy young girl sings with pride and confidence on a road trip with the family of her best friend. Her best friend's older sister comments on how terrible the shy young girl sounds while singing. It wasn't meant to be a life-changing comment, but the shy young girl never sings in front of people again.

Event: Insult by someone admired
Belief (assumption made): *I am a terrible singer*
Result: Withdraw from ever singing in front of people again
Evidence of fact: One snarky comment from a teenage girl

Example Two: A shy young girl tries out for the eighth grade basketball team. Sixty-two other participants try out for the team, but there is only room for sixty girls. After days of practice the shy young girl is cut, along with one other classmate. Humiliated, the young girl never went out for another sport again because she assumed she was not an athlete.

Event: Being cut from the basketball team
Belief (assumption made): *I am not an athlete*
Result: Never tries out for another group sport
Evidence of fact: Not excelling in one sport

Example Three: A shy young girl sits through most of her primary and secondary school years feeling out of place, never quite grasping what is being taught, or ever finding her rhythm to learning. School was a compulsory exercise that provided very little internal reward and left her feeling inadequate and unteachable.

Event: Primary and Secondary Education
Belief (assumption made): *I am not a very smart person*
Result: Stopped education after high school graduation
Evidence of Fact: Not excelling in the traditional school setting

What if I told you the shy young girl in the above examples was me? What if I further told you that the result was only temporary? That's right, my best friend's sister told me I had a terrible singing voice and for years I refused to even open my mouth and sing at church, until one day my belief was trumped by my love of singing! I changed my result because I changed my belief. I found ranges, and songs that were better suited to my voice, and now I am a little songbird. That basketball team experience? I allowed that belief to rob me of group sports for the rest of my high school years. The belief I formed that I was not an athlete was trumped by my love of being physical. Once I found weight lifting, running, tennis, hiking, biking, and kayaking, I realized that one sport does not dictate whether or not I am an athlete. And finally, my education... I did not learn like other students, and I would come to discover that I have a form of dyslexia that makes comprehension extremely difficult. However, my curiosity trumped my dyslexia, and at nineteen I discovered auditory learning. Auditory learning, coupled with reading techniques to adjust to my dyslexia, has finally provided an avenue to quench my appetite for learning. I may not excel in the traditional classroom setting, but that in no way indicates my level of intelligence. My curiosity has proven to be my greatest gift, and I am grateful for that. I will be a lifetime learner!

My grateful, loyal Green Zone Thinking mind is urging me to follow up my three disempowering, limiting belief stories with one of my most empowering beliefs, handed to me as a little girl by my Aunt Billie. As I have mentioned before, I was a very curious child blessed to have in my life a number of elders who loved and cared for me. My Aunt Billie was one of those special people in my young life. One summer, my cousin Rusty and I were spending the night with my Aunt Billie on her farm in Louisiana. Rusty and I were probably five or six years old, and I am sure we had played our hearts out on the farm that day. In my childhood, bedtime was always very special. The female caregivers in my life (my Nanny, Aunt Billie, Aunt Mildred, and Momma) never just put us kids to bed; they always laid with us, talked to us, prayed with us and listened to our thoughts. This night at Aunt Billie's was no different.

As the three of us lay together laughing and giggling, asking questions and listening, my Aunt Billie gently took my face in her hands, looked at me in the eyes and said with such confidence, "Robin Michaela, you are going to be a minister one day. You have a minister's heart." I have never, ever forgotten that moment. I felt chosen, special, and empowered, and from that day forward, I knew God was going to direct me in a special way.

Using the same logic I used in the limiting belief examples, let's look at how this empowering belief was formed.

Event: Empowering words spoken to me by someone I admired
Belief (assumption made): *I was chosen by God to do good work*
Result: Living life trying to honor this gift
Evidence of Fact: One simple sentence spoken to me by someone I admired

As you can see, beliefs are delicate. They shape and form what we believe ourselves to be and do, determined by a simple, seemingly meaningless moment. I outlined for you three of my most disempowering beliefs, beliefs that, for a time, held me back and defined my limits. I also shared with you one of my most powerful beliefs, a belief that has given me the courage to dream larger than life. All of these examples became part of my belief system in an instant. My belief system wasn't interested in whether or not my newly formed belief empowered or disempowered me — my brain was simply looking for perceived patterns to help form intentional actions.

For example, in the limiting beliefs I formed, embarrassment (pain) was the trigger. My hormonal reaction to the pain of embarrassment was so strong that it alerted my belief system to mark the event(s). My brain then began forming intentional actions to avoid ever feeling that pain again. On the flipside, my empowering belief was formed in much the same way. The emotion I felt through the kind words my Aunt Billie said to me was my trigger. My hormonal reaction to the emotion was so strong that it alerted my belief system to mark the event. My brain then began forming intentional actions to encourage feeling this emotion as often as possible.

I work on my limiting beliefs daily as part of my commitment to personal growth and expansion. I ask myself, "Is this a limiting belief I inherited, or is it something created from a past experience?" I try to get the bottom of my limiting beliefs so I can either release them, redirect them, or reinvent them. The only beliefs I nourish are the ones that help me serve the highest idea of myself.

What are some of your limiting beliefs? Do your beliefs serve you or limit you? Wouldn't it be fun to identify every limiting belief you hold, find the source, discredit the source, and reinvent your belief to serve you! A great tool to use when trying to determine whether or not a belief is valid is the H.A.P.P.I.N.E.S.S. Ladder. If the belief has a low vibration that is somewhere in the Red or Yellow Zone on the H.A.P.P.I.N.E.S.S. Ladder, release it. All three of the limiting beliefs I mentioned felt terrible every time I thought of them. Your beliefs should empower you, not disempower you. Find the resonance of your belief and either move it up the ladder to the Green Zone or release it completely.

Beliefs are formed in moments, and those moments can be rather insignificant. Yet we internalize the moments, make a broad brush assumption and live as if our assumption is law. We dismiss our desires and our potential, and we use our beliefs to protect us from pain. Now that we know who the players are in the game of expectations, let's begin outlining a system that you can use to redefine your expectation from a place of Joy and Inspiration.

Food for Thought

Several years ago, my niece asked me to train her and a few friends in the gym over summer break. I was thrilled — exercise and nutrition have been my ministry for as long as I remember, and spending time with my niece is one of the greatest joys of my life, so, of course, I agreed without hesitation. My niece is a stunning young girl with the most mesmerizing, sparkly, crystal blue eyes. She is extremely athletic, with broad shoulders, muscular legs, small chest and waist, and a strong back. She is 5 feet 3 inches of shear power and force, like a gymnast. Her physique was the envy of many young girls, but despite that, one day she said something to me in the gym that made me realize how destructive unexamined admiration could be.

We were taking progress measurements in the locker room and she grabbed my arm and pulled it away from my body toward hers. She said, "Ronnie, I want muscles like yours, long and lean. I hate my little, short arms." I grabbed her and hugged her and began explaining to her what I am about to explain to you. Despite how beautiful and perfect she is in her own skin, she desired different results based off of misunderstood admiration.

The next part of this chapter is the missing link for so many in setting healthy, aligned expectations. Get ready to discover what your belief system already knows. Once you accept this as your truth, your beliefs and your desires will fall into the perfect rhythm of complementing and supporting each other allowing you to transform in a state of Joy and Inspiration and releasing you from the grasp of toxic comparison.

Let me introduce you to the three different body types that establish the platform for all body types: **Ectomorph**, **Mesomorph**, and **Endomorph**. The main differences between the three body types are metabolism speed and bone structure. Although you'll learn about each one individually, realize that the majority of us are a combination of the body types. It is important to understand each type and know which type (or combination) you are genetically predisposed to prior to setting expectations. Why is this so important? It will help you understand why certain aspects of diet and exercise are harder and slower or easier and quicker for you than they are for other people.

Knowing your body type is such an important piece of information that will help you set goals and expectations that are aligned with the highest and best use of your natural resources. When you understand your body, your beliefs and your desires begin working together.

Food for Thought

Does your body type dictate your overall health? Absolutely, positively not! Another cultural meme that is very destructive is the idea that if you are skinny you are healthy and if you are fat you are unhealthy; that is just not true. I want to introduce you to a new medical term, a term that I have felt in my bones for a long time and am excited to see the medical community put a language to. This term and the findings that accompany it will, finally, begin to break down the cultural meme of fat=unhealthy and skinny=healthy. The term I am speaking of is MONW (Metabolically Obese Normal Weight) or Skinny Fat Syndrome. It means you are under lean but over fat, and it is the gateway to serious health deficiencies such as diabetes, heart disease, heart attack, stroke, and even cancer and dementia. As a matter of fact, studies show it is healthier to be fat and fit than thin and out of shape! Regardless of the body type, every body type benefits from proper care.   The skinny, ectomorph, the out-of-shape mesomorph, or the obese endomorph all share one thing: they each benefit from a balanced diet and exercise. No "body" is immune from disease.

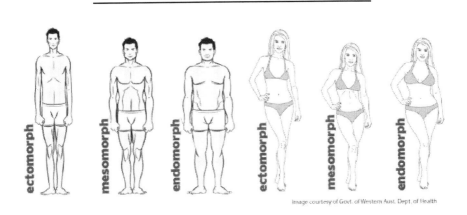

Image courtesy of Govt. of Western Aust. Dept. of Health

Now let's uncover each body type in detail.

Ectomorph:

Have you ever known someone that can eat whatever they want and rarely if ever gain weight? Some people gain weight by simply staring at a particular food for too long, but some are able to easily gain muscle and maintain a lean body. Genetics is at the crux of these patterns.

An Ectomorph body type is characterized by a small frame, whether short or tall. Ectomorph's have a slight frame and build, very low body fat and typically a very high metabolism. Some of their characteristics:

- Weight gain is hard
- Delicate build
- Females tend to be flat-chested
- Fragile appearance
- Lean
- Lightly muscled
- Small shoulders
- Long thin limbs

Before the Fork

Popular examples of famous Ectomorphs would be:
Male: Jim Parsons, Adam Levine, Jimmy Stewart
Female: Cameron Diaz, Audrey Hepburn, Angelina Jolie

Mesomorph:

A Mesomorph is characterized by an athletic, sporty frame, broad shoulders, nice square shoulders, visibly defined muscle, and very good posture. Mesomorph body types respond best to weight training, and their ability to gain muscle can be seen quickly. Characteristics of a Mesomorph are:
- Athletic
- Hard bodied with well-defined muscle
- Rectangular body shape
- Strong
- Great body symmetry
- Quickly gain muscle
- Gain weight more quickly than Ectomorphs

Popular examples of famous Mesomorphs would be:
Male: David Beckham, Mark Wahlberg, Ryan Reynolds, Hugh Jackman
Female: Jillian Michaels, Jessica Biel, Halle Berry, Pink

Endomorph:

An endomorph is characterized by a solid frame and a well-defined, strong, rounded shoulders. Endomorphs typically gain fat more easily than the other two body types, but they are the strongest of the three. Characteristics of the endomorph:
- Soft and round body
- Gains muscle and fat both easily
- Slower metabolism makes it more difficult to lose weight.
- Medium, large joints and bones
- Body fat tends to settle in the lower regions of the body, mainly the lower abdomen and the rear end, hips, and thighs.

Popular examples of famous Endomorphs are:
Male: Jack Black, Seth Rogan, and maybe even Vin Diesel
Female: Oprah Winfrey, Jennifer Lopez, Jennifer Hudson

Now remember, it is most likely that each of us, as well as the popular examples above, are actually a combination of the three body types. The odds of anyone fitting perfectly into one category is rare. You can probably identify with traits from one or two groups.

Let's put an end to the negative stigma of body types and begin to develop the best and highest idea regardless of the body type you identify with most. I myself am probably 75% Mesomorph and 25% Endomorph, and I love it. My baby sister is 90% Ectomorph and 10% Mesomorph, and my big sister is probably 60% Endomorph and 40% Mesomorph. We're all made up of our own unique puzzle pieces, and one puzzle is no better than the other.

Knowing the pieces you are working with is instrumental in aligning your beliefs and desires, and setting expectations that serve you. Although the majority of information we covered in this chapter has been physical, your expectations extend far beyond the physical. With this new knowledge, take a step back and reexamine your personal expectations, both physical and emotional. Acknowledge the role desire has played in your life and how it has felt when your desires and beliefs are not in alignment. Be patient in the process of aligning your beliefs and desires; there are many thought patterns that must be interrupted and redirected to blend the two ideas.

You will know when your beliefs and desires are in alignment through the joy you will find in every step of the transformation process. By blending the two players, beliefs and desires, in the game of expectations you have removed your biggest roadblock: yourself. Use the H.A.P.P.I.N.E.S.S. Ladder to determine how closely aligned your beliefs and desires are at any given time. When there is alignment between your beliefs and desires, you will feel free of the heavy, negative resistance. Your energy will move more quickly, and you will experience the high impact, contagious, life-affirming state of being found at the top of the H.A.P.P.I.N.E.S.S. Ladder.

In conclusion, I want to remind you of an earlier point regarding our emotions: There is no elevator to the top of the H.A.P.P.I.N.E.S.S. Ladder, and the same rule applies to climbing the ladder of expectations. You are looking at yourself through a new set of lens, and you are aligning new ideas and getting rid of old, cultural memes. Allow yourself room to grow. As my body is aging and my hormones are changing it seems every morning I am meeting a new Robin in the mirror. I embrace her with all the love my heart can muster, but I would be lying if I said the cellulite doesn't bother me!

If you follow my techniques and my teachings, the vision you create of your Desired Self today will evolve through confidence. As your confidence grows, your desire will shift (just as we discussed earlier); the destination will become a moving target holding your attention long enough to keep you moving forward. The most important take-away from our final pillar, Expectations, is this: If you line up your beliefs and desires, learn how to use comparison to support you, and dismiss uncomfortable comparisons that leave you feeling defeated, you will always find Joy. Finally, you will always (and I mean always) honor your beliefs above anything else!

On a bright and sunny day over a decade ago, I collapsed in my hall and rose a changed person. When I stood up from the floor in my hallway, I had everything I needed to change my life and the life of my family. I had it all along; I just didn't know how to access it. Over the course of the next few years I felt called to share my experience with others, so I went to work trying to put a language to my experience. Well, it ends up, there is more than a language; there is a system. A clearly defined, actionable system handed to me through a moment of divine alignment. A system that just "IS," much like gravity. It just is. In order to build a language so that I could explain my system, first I had to identify the players and the rules of the game. This was not an overnight process; I have poured over fourteen years into determining only the most vital pieces to the transformation puzzle.

The Six Pillars of Support made my transformation possible. Each pillar played a vital role in my transformation. The pillars supported a new attitude, made me accountable in a non-condemning way, provided me with healthy boundaries both physically and nutritionally, helped me find the emotional support I needed, and finally taught me how to set expectations that brought out the best in me. These Six Pillars of Support have been my constant companion, and anytime I feel wobbly, I look to see if my foundation is in place. I am forever grateful for the role these pillars provide in my life.

I can think of no better example to move us into the next section of the book than that of Mother Nature. If our pillars support our transformation — much like oxygen, gravity, food and water support our life on earth — then the four phases of transformation are the seasons. In the next section we will walk through the Four Phases of Transformation and discover why each season is necessary, what to expect during each season, and finally what to do at the end of the final season.

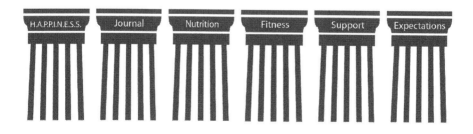

SECTION THREE

The Four Phases of Transformation and the 28-Day Experience

Phase One: Get Real/Discover, Day 1 through 3
Phase Two: Get Right/Recognize, Day 4 through 20
Phase Three: Get With It/Reinvent, Day 21 through 24
Phase Four: Go Live It/Enjoy, Day 25 through 28

"Once upon a time you had a dream.
Today that dream turned into a plan.
Will it be easy?
NO. Will it be enlightening? ILLUMINATING.
Will it be worth it? ABSOLUTELY."
- Robin Shea

The Four Phases of Transformation

Below is an overview of each phase, but in Section Three you will actually move through the Four Phases of Transformation in the 28-Day Experience.

Phase One: Get Real / Discover
During this phase, you will:
- Identify your Why Story.
- Put your system in place and identify all the pieces to the transformation puzzle (Your Why Story, Six Pillars of Support, Four Phases of Transformation).
- Acknowledge and commit to becoming a student of change by committing to tracking behavior, identifying obstacles (people, places and things), and learning to "let go" of resistance through the use of the H.A.P.P.I.N.E.S.S. Ladder.

Phase Two: Get Right / Recognize
During this phase, you will:
- Learn how to implement changes.
- Continue to focus on subconscious behavior patterns through journaling and the practice of Process/Performance Visualization, and Reflection and Projected Imagery.
- Sharpen your Why Story, refine the Tips, Tools, and Techniques that best work for your individual challenges, practice climbing up the H.A.P.P.I.N.E.S.S. Ladder, and begin looking for signs of newly evolving default behaviors.

Phase Three: Get With It / Reinvent
During this phase, you will:
- Begin refining tips, tools and techniques that promote growth and change.
- Begin to appreciate contrast and seek it out in order to consciously redirect your behavior.
- Reinforce and strengthen your new habits.

Phase Four: Go Live It / Enjoy
During this phase, you will:
- Reflect on your journey and what you've learned.
- Celebrate establishing new, healthy habits.
- Rest and recharge to begin Phase One again.

"Once upon a time you had a dream. Today that dream turned into a plan."
- *Robin Shea*

You've created your "why" story and taken the fork in the road, good for you!
Phase One: Get Real lasts three days. During this period, you are preparing
your home, schedule, and mind to move into Phase Two.

Goal:

Below I have provided you with a checklist. The goal is to go over your
checklist and make sure you have everything in place to launch into
your new "chosen" weight-loss and fitness program.

Action Steps:

Safeguard your home environment by cleaning out your pantry, and
refrigerator, be thorough, and complete!

Based on research from Cornell University Food and Brand Lab and
the work of Dr. Brian Wansick, there are things we can do in our home
environment that will assist us in making better choices at home and
set us up for success with less conscious effort.

- **Snack Tower** - In my home, this is what I do: All approved snacks, and
  quick grab-n-go's are visible and kept in a snack tower in the corner
  of my kitchen. My tower has three baskets. One basket for quick grab-n-go snacks like nuts, fruit, and some snack bars. Another basket
  is for breads, nut-butters, and honey. In the largest bottom basket, I
  keep seasonal fruit that doesn't require refrigeration. The addition of
  the snack tower in my kitchen over ten years ago transformed how I

grocery shopped and how my family nourished itself. It simplifies grocery shopping because, at-a-glance, I can see what we are low on and replenish the tower. It helps us eat better because convenience is a strong human driver. Statistically, we will eat what is most conveniently located, so this eliminates pantry rummaging completely.

- **The Family Kitchen:** Ideally, you will take your family along with you on this healthful journey; however, I understand if unwilling participants make this a difficult challenge. Two thoughts I would like to leave you with regarding the Family Kitchen: If your children (and spouse) perceive your new nutritional program as a punishment, rather than a new healthy lifestyle, they will associate pain to transformation. Maybe the first time through the 28-Day Experience you should focus on YOU alone, and as you grow in confidence and skill, you can extend the practice into your Family Kitchen where everyone will benefit from the new healthy parameters.

- **Clearing Your Schedule to Exercise:** Try several different times of day to find your rhythm. Keep your workout gear visible in your vehicle, like in the seat next to you, and not in your trunk. This increases your chances of success. Pick your classes and accountability partner and set your schedule to show up.

- **Grocery Shopping 101:** Never grocery shop on an empty stomach. Thirty minutes after eating is best. Allow yourself an extra hour in the store to get familiar with the brands and items unique to your chosen weight loss program.

- **Rest and Hydration:** Allow yourself extra rest. You are moving through a lot of change, help your body support you by providing it with extra rest. Always stay hydrated. This will benefit both your desired weight loss as well as recovery from exercise.

The first three days of the program are INTENSE, but I have faith that you will put in the effort. The most important thing to remember during Phase One is this: Keep these things very close and never skip a day of journaling the process. I have provided journal pages for each day of the 28 days in the Four Phases of Transformation; to help get you started, use the Tips, Tools, and Techniques section located in the index to help find creative ways to enhance your mental rehearsal practice, state of being practices, home, social and on-the-go tips, identifying saboteurs and more. Once you are feeling more confident, you will begin building your own unique tips, tools, and techniques.

So far, we've have gone on quite a journey together. I shared the intimate details of my life and what led up to my personal transformation. We dove into the thirteen years I spent researching the connection between spirituality, neuroscience, and behavioral science. Lastly, I decoded my findings into a teachable system. In Section Three I will walk you through a 28-Day Experience of the Four Phases of Transformation. You will experience for yourself the magic in joining together Spiritual, Behavioral and Neuroscience and the role Joy and Happiness play in lasting change.

I presented the architecture of my program in its entirety, and you now know everything I know. But, as we've discussed, knowledge is not enough. Knowledge is only a seed, plant it in the richest emotional soil possible and watch it grow.

Is your Why Story in place? Is it strong, can you feel the energy pulling you toward your vision? If not, build a stronger story.

Here is how this section works: I have prepared a message for each of the twenty-eight days. The message will align with the spiritual, behavioral, and neurological aspects of change for that phase. Following the message, there will be blank journal pages for you to record your journey to change. Here are a few things to think about before we start.

- Have your Why Story in place
- Use the Tips, Tools, and Techniques section located in the index to help find creative ways to enhance your mental rehearsal practice, state of being practices, home, social and on-the-go tips, identifying saboteurs and more. Once you are feeling more confident, you will begin building your unique tips, tools, and techniques.
- Use the book, reflect back to previous chapters, and stay engaged.
- Keep your pillars close (especially the H.A.P.P.I.N.E.S.S. Ladder) and remember: Perfection doesn't exist, so shoot for a little better every day.

This is my journey...

MY THOUGHTS DETERMINE WHO I AM,

WHAT I HAVE,

AND WHAT I CAN DO.

THE POWER TO DECIDE MY LIFE RESTS INSIDE OF ME

THROUGH THE HOLY SPIRIT AND I BOLDLY CLAIM

MY RIGHT TO LIVE WITH GRACE AND GLORY ON MY SIDE.

MY THOUGHTS WILL REFLECT A LOVE FOR MYSELF ONLY EQUALED

BY GOD'S LOVE FOR ME.

My mind is alert.

MY HEART IS OPEN AND JOY AND HAPPINESS ARE MY GUIDING LIGHTS.

AMEN.

DAILY BLESSINGS

Get Real With Robin
Stop Hiding Behind Your Bullshit Excuses!

H.A.P.P.I.N.E.S.S. Ladder
1. Are you looking for ways during your day to raise your vibration, or are you still blaming others for your emotions?
2. Do you take time each day to find something to be grateful for, or do you find yourself coveting the lives of others?
3. Do you find yourself craving Green Zone emotions and redirecting your thinking to support this state of being, or do you find yourself feeding your toxic emotions through gossip, negative self talk, and self-sabotage?

Today's H.A.P.P.I.N.E.S.S. Non-Negotiable: Commit to one thing you can do differently today that will help you maintain your Green Zone Emotions.
For example: I am committed to maintaining a positive attitude despite the hostility at work.

Discovery through Journaling
1. Are you faithfully committed to your journaling practice, or are you playing catch up every few days?
2. Do you take time each day to practice your mental rehearsal, or do you skip this exercise all together?
3. Are you identifying obstacles and creating tools for yourself, or are missing opportunities to better handle your vulnerabilities?

Today's Journaling Non-Negotiable: Commit to one thing you can do differently today that will help you maintain thorough journal pages.
For example: I am committed to scheduling out time to ensure I get enough journaling in.

Nutrition
1. Are you loyal to the guidelines laid out in your nutritional plan, or are you loosely interpreting the guidelines?
2. Are you pre-planning your meals and committing adequate shopping and meal prep time, or are you shopping on the fly, fitting it in when you can?
3. Do you find yourself excited that you have found your "forever" nutrition plan, or are you still having a difficult time imaging living within these nutritional guidelines for the rest of your life?

Today's Nutrition Non-Negotiable: Commit to one thing you can do differently today that will help you maintain your nutritional commitment.
For example: I am committed to prepping my lunch for the day so I don't eat unhealthy at work.

Fitness
1. Are you honoring the time you set aside each day to focus on your physical fitness, or are you still planning to start tomorrow?
2. Are you finding it easier to prioritize your fitness above other less important activities, or are you allowing those activities to edge out your fitness?
3. Have you successfully rearranged your schedule to allow fitness to flow more effortlessly into your life, or are you still trying to figure out where to fit it in?
Today's Fitness Non-Negotiable: Commit to one thing you can do differently today that will help you maintain your fitness commitment.
For example: I am committed to showing up early to my fitness class so I have time to warm up.

Support
1. Are you happily engaged with a group that supports your growth, or are you still sharing your struggles with people that are ill-equipped to support you?
2. Have you let people off the hook who do not possess the skills to lend support, like family and friends, or are you still using them as an excuse for holding you back?
3. Is your new support system spending more time on building problem solving tools than anything else, or is your new support group reinforcing the problems spending very little time on creating tools?

Today's Support Non-Negotiable: Commit to one thing you can do differently today that will help you maintain your commitment to receiving support.
For example: I am committed to reaching out to someone for positive accountability.

Expectations
1. Are you feeling a deep appreciation for the body you were given, or are you still disappointed you aren't built like others?
2. Are you free of judging yourself against the accomplishments of others, or are you still using an external measuring stick to beat yourself over the head with?

3. Are noticing others that share your body type and aligning your goals with your strengths, or are you still using an unaligned body type and setting your goals based on unachievable or unmaintainable characteristics out of alignment with your strengths?

Today's Expectations Non-Negotiable: Commit to one thing you can do differently today that will help you maintain your healthy commitment to expectations.

For example: I am committed to appreciating one new thing about my body today.

28-DAY EXPERIENCE

Use the following journal pages to reflect on and record your daily journey through the Four Phases of Transformation in areas of Nutrition, Fitness, Support, and Expectations.

This is my journey...

MY THOUGHTS DETERMINE WHO I AM,

WHAT I HAVE,

AND WHAT I CAN DO.

THE POWER TO DECIDE MY LIFE RESTS INSIDE OF ME

THROUGH THE HOLY SPIRIT AND I BOLDLY CLAIM

MY RIGHT TO LIVE WITH GRACE AND GLORY ON MY SIDE.

MY THOUGHTS WILL REFLECT A LOVE FOR MYSELF ONLY EQUALED

BY GOD'S LOVE FOR ME.

My mind is alert.

MY HEART IS OPEN AND JOY AND HAPPINESS ARE MY GUIDING LIGHTS.

AMEN.

DAILY BLESSINGS

Day One: Phase One

There is a mathematical equation for everything, even changing your life. I'm no mathematician, but I have come up with a formula that has never let me down yet. The formula is $C^3 = F \times T$.

C^3 stands for Inspired Change, which is the only change I am interested in. I use Change to the power of three because, in order to feel truly Inspired to Change in a state of Joy and Inspiration, three elements must be working together.

Spirit + Mind + Brain

Spirit refers to the knowing that you are acting in alignment with your Desired Self (Spirituality).

Mind, as I use it here, refers to the brain "At Work" (Neuroscience).

The brain does not create joy or happiness; it merely reflects back to us what we are reflecting to it through our emotions (Behavioral Science).

The F in the Formula stands for FAITH.
Faith is not about believing in the unknown. Faith refers to the knowing of your potential and your goodness. Faith is seeing with your emotions and trusting your emotions as your inner guidance system. Faith is knowing what the God within you knows without life having to prove it to you.

The T in the Formula stands for TIMELESSNESS
Timelessness refers to the lessening of a sense of urgency. Timelessness happens when the journey becomes more important than the destination.

"Your potential to achieve INSPIRED CHANGE is a factor of the FAITH you have in trusting your emotions as your inner guidance system, multiplied by the TIMELESSNESS you embrace in your journey!" - Robin Shea

GROUND YOUR DAY IN THESE POSITIVE PRACTICES...

DISCOVERY THROUGH JOURNALING

Catalyst Goal - "Shooting Star Goals"

LIST YOUR SHORT-TERM, FEEL-GOOD GOAL FOR THE DAY: _____

_____

_____

Process/Performance Visualization - "Preview of Success"

LIST 3 PROCESS AND/OR PERFORMANCE STRUGGLES:

1. _____

2. _____

3. _____

LIST 3 WAYS YOU ENVISION YOURSELF OVERCOMING THESE 3 OBSTACLES:

1. _____

2. _____

3. _____

Projected Visualization - "Future Self Meditation"

LIST 3 "FUTURE SELF" SCENARIOS IN WHICH YOU ARE LIVING YOUR ENVISIONED LIFE.

1. _____

2. _____

3. _____

Expectations and Custom Goal Setting

☐ MY EXPECTATIONS ARE LINING UP WITH MY BELIEF SYSTEM.

LIST 3 "I AM" STATEMENTS:

1. _____

2. _____

3. _____

Reflection – "The Day's Lessons"

EVENT:——————————————————————————————————

STUMBLE:——————————————————————————————————

TOOL:——————————————————————————————————

——————————————————————————————————

——————————————————————————————————

——————————————————————————————————

——————————————————————————————————

H.A.P.P.I.N.E.S.S. Victories

LIST 3 EMOTIONAL VICTORIES YOU ACHIEVED TODAY:

1. ——————————————————————————————————

2. ——————————————————————————————————

3. ——————————————————————————————————

NUTRITION

☐ I AM HONORING MY BODY BY HONORING THE GUIDELINES OF MY NUTRITIONAL PLAN.

FITNESS

☐ I AM HONORING MY BODY BY HONORING MY SELECTED FITNESS PLAN.

SUPPORT

☐ I AM RECEIVING SUPPORT

☐ I AM GIVING SUPPORT

LIST 3 PEOPLE YOU RECEIVE SUPPORT FROM OR PROVIDE SUPPORT TO:

1. ——————————————————————————————————

2. ——————————————————————————————————

3. ——————————————————————————————————

MY SUPPORT TEAM IS:

☐ SAFE

☐ EMPATHETIC

☐ SOLUTION-FOCUSED

This is my journey...

MY THOUGHTS DETERMINE WHO I AM,

WHAT I HAVE,

AND WHAT I CAN DO.

THE POWER TO DECIDE MY LIFE RESTS INSIDE OF ME

THROUGH THE HOLY SPIRIT AND I BOLDLY CLAIM

MY RIGHT TO LIVE WITH GRACE AND GLORY ON MY SIDE.

MY THOUGHTS WILL REFLECT A LOVE FOR MYSELF ONLY EQUALED

BY GOD'S LOVE FOR ME.

My mind is alert.

MY HEART IS OPEN AND JOY AND HAPPINESS ARE MY GUIDING LIGHTS.

AMEN.

DAILY BLESSINGS

Day Two: Phase One

So many people approach lifestyle transformation like it is a wishing well. They kiss a coin and toss it into the well WISHING for a miracle. Wishing will change nothing...

Wishing is a first cousin to Hope, and while both may feel good, you must breathe life into them through action. Action is what separates those that "dream" from those that "realize their dreams." Today is where wishing and hoping STOPS and ACTION born of passion begins.

You are leaving the town of Familiar, and there is work to be done. You have an old friend that has signed up to go on this journey with you, Uncomfortable. You used to love hanging out with Uncomfortable! That's how you learned how to walk, talk, dance, skip, and more. But over time the fear of being laughed at, falling, or failing drowned out the joy that being uncomfortable brought into your life. Remember your old friend; he is here to help you by bringing old fears and doubts to the surface so you can learn to redirect them. The quicker you change your attitude about being uncomfortable the quicker you will master this new land of change.

Feeling Uncomfortable from the Red Zone vs. Feeling Uncomfortable from the Green Zone makes all the difference. Red Zone fear feels intimidating, shameful, and disempowering. Green Zone fear feels exciting, light-hearted, rewarding, and empowering.

Until next time... LIVE INSPIRED!

"WITH EVERY RISING OF THE SUN, THINK OF YOUR LIFE AS JUST BEGUN..."

-ROBIN SHEA

GROUND YOUR DAY IN THESE POSITIVE PRACTICES...

DISCOVERY THROUGH JOURNALING

Catalyst Goal - "Shooting Star Goals"

LIST YOUR SHORT-TERM, FEEL-GOOD GOAL FOR THE DAY: _____

_____

_____

Process/Performance Visualization - "Preview of Success"

LIST 3 PROCESS AND/ OR PERFORMANCE STRUGGLES:

1. _____
2. _____
3. _____

LIST 3 WAYS YOU ENVISION YOURSELF OVERCOMING THESE 3 OBSTACLES:

1. _____
2. _____
3. _____

Projected Visualization - "Future Self Meditation"

LIST 3 "FUTURE SELF" SCENARIOS IN WHICH YOU ARE LIVING YOUR ENVISIONED LIFE.

1. _____
2. _____
3. _____

Expectations and Custom Goal Setting

☐ MY EXPECTATIONS ARE LINING UP WITH MY BELIEF SYSTEM.

LIST 3 "I AM" STATEMENTS:

1. _____
2. _____
3. _____

Reflection – "The Day's Lessons"

EVENT:——————————————————————————————

STUMBLE:——————————————————————————————

TOOL:——————————————————————————————

———————————————————————————————————

———————————————————————————————————

———————————————————————————————————

———————————————————————————————————

H.A.P.P.I.N.E.S.S. Victories

LIST 3 EMOTIONAL VICTORIES YOU ACHIEVED TODAY:

1. ————————————————————————————————

2. ————————————————————————————————

3. ————————————————————————————————

NUTRITION

☐ I AM HONORING MY BODY BY HONORING THE GUIDELINES OF MY NUTRITIONAL PLAN.

FITNESS

☐ I AM HONORING MY BODY BY HONORING MY SELECTED FITNESS PLAN.

SUPPORT

☐ I AM RECEIVING SUPPORT

☐ I AM GIVING SUPPORT

LIST 3 PEOPLE YOU RECEIVE SUPPORT FROM OR PROVIDE SUPPORT TO:

1. ————————————————————————————————

2. ————————————————————————————————

3. ————————————————————————————————

MY SUPPORT TEAM IS:

☐ SAFE

☐ EMPATHETIC

☐ SOLUTION-FOCUSED

This is my journey...

MY THOUGHTS DETERMINE WHO I AM,

WHAT I HAVE,

AND WHAT I CAN DO.

THE POWER TO DECIDE MY LIFE RESTS INSIDE OF ME

THROUGH THE HOLY SPIRIT AND I BOLDLY CLAIM

MY RIGHT TO LIVE WITH GRACE AND GLORY ON MY SIDE.

MY THOUGHTS WILL REFLECT A LOVE FOR MYSELF ONLY EQUALED

BY GOD'S LOVE FOR ME.

My mind is alert.

MY HEART IS OPEN AND JOY AND HAPPINESS ARE MY GUIDING LIGHTS.

AMEN.

DAILY BLESSINGS

Day Three: Phase One

I know you are anxious to get started, however, investing time gaining a working knowledge of the transformation process will prove to be invaluable. Having a clear understanding of the following will better prepare you for the more vulnerable phases of the transformation process, which begins on Day Four.

Your Why Story
Do you have a compelling, emotionally charged Why Story?

H.A.P.P.I.N.E.S.S. Ladder: Finding Joy in the Journey -
Are you excited to try and redirect negative emotion at every opportunity?

Discovery through Journaling -
Are you committed to journaling your way through this 28-day process?

Nutrition: Setting Healthy Nutritional Parameters -
Do you have your nutrition plan in place?
Have you safeguarded your home, office, etc.?

Fitness, Setting Healthy Fitness Parameters -
Do you have your fitness plan in place?

Support, Your Emotional Support System -
Have you identified your support system?

Setting Your Expectations —
Are you in alignment with the highest and best version of yourself?

If you answered the above questions with "yes," you are ready to move forward. Tomorrow launches Phase Two, the most challenging phase of Lifestyle Transformation. Lean into these six pillars with trust and confidence knowing that you are not alone and everything you are experiencing is just as it should be.

Until next time, LIVE INSPIRED!

GROUND YOUR DAY IN THESE POSITIVE PRACTICES...

DISCOVERY THROUGH JOURNALING

Catalyst Goal - "Shooting Star Goals"

LIST YOUR SHORT-TERM, FEEL-GOOD GOAL FOR THE DAY: _____

_____

_____

Process/Performance Visualization - "Preview of Success"

LIST 3 PROCESS AND/ OR PERFORMANCE STRUGGLES:

1. _____

2. _____

3. _____

LIST 3 WAYS YOU ENVISION YOURSELF OVERCOMING THESE 3 OBSTACLES:

1. _____

2. _____

3. _____

Projected Visualization - "Future Self Meditation"

LIST 3 "FUTURE SELF" SCENARIOS IN WHICH YOU ARE LIVING YOUR ENVISIONED LIFE.

1. _____

2. _____

3. _____

Expectations and Custom Goal Setting

☐   MY EXPECTATIONS ARE LINING UP WITH MY BELIEF SYSTEM.

LIST 3 "I AM" STATEMENTS:

1. _____

2. _____

3. _____

Reflection – "The Day's Lessons"

EVENT:

STUMBLE:

TOOL:

H.A.P.P.I.N.E.S.S. Victories

LIST 3 EMOTIONAL VICTORIES YOU ACHIEVED TODAY:

1.

2.

3.

NUTRITION

☐ I AM HONORING MY BODY BY HONORING THE GUIDELINES OF MY NUTRITIONAL PLAN.

FITNESS

☐ I AM HONORING MY BODY BY HONORING MY SELECTED FITNESS PLAN.

SUPPORT

☐ I AM RECEIVING SUPPORT

☐ I AM GIVING SUPPORT

LIST 3 PEOPLE YOU RECEIVE SUPPORT FROM OR PROVIDE SUPPORT TO:

1.

2.

3.

MY SUPPORT TEAM IS:

☐ SAFE

☐ EMPATHETIC

☐ SOLUTION-FOCUSED

This is my journey...

MY THOUGHTS DETERMINE WHO I AM,

WHAT I HAVE,

AND WHAT I CAN DO.

THE POWER TO DECIDE MY LIFE RESTS INSIDE OF ME

THROUGH THE HOLY SPIRIT AND I BOLDLY CLAIM

MY RIGHT TO LIVE WITH GRACE AND GLORY ON MY SIDE.

MY THOUGHTS WILL REFLECT A LOVE FOR MYSELF ONLY EQUALED

BY GOD'S LOVE FOR ME.

My mind is alert.

MY HEART IS OPEN AND JOY AND HAPPINESS ARE MY GUIDING LIGHTS.

AMEN.

DAILY BLESSINGS

Day Four: Phase Two

You just left the Land of Familiar... How does it feel to be 100% committed to the Land of Change?

Are you confident, focused, directed? Do you understand that struggle is your best teacher and tools are born from struggle?

Today will be a high-octane day for you, and you will be running on two parts excitement, one part fear, and one part confusion. Here are a couple of things to remember as you enter the Wasteland:

Food for Thought

1. **Automatic Subconscious Behaviors** - These will sneak up on you and sabotage you before you even realize it is happening. If this happens, stop the default behavior, bless it for rearing its head, forgive yourself for being human and redirect. Don't beat yourself up! This is very important — the hormones released during the Red Zone emotions of self-loathing or negative self-talk are extremely toxic and will leave you searching for other destructive default behaviors to self-soothe. Interrupt this pattern by extending forgiveness right away.
2. **Focus** - Find a way to keep your conscious mind engaged in the process of change as much as possible. Remember, out of a twelve-hour day you use your conscious mind only 40 minutes — the rest of the time you are on auto-pilot. Typical no longer exists; you are asking much more of your conscious mind than ever before. A great way to add conscious hours into your day is to Journal several times during the day. Every time you journal, you engage your conscious mind outside of its normal use strengthening your ability to stay present. These do not have to be long journal entries, just short observations, lessons, situations, etc.
3. **Begin a Daily Meditation Practice** - For more on this practice, check the Tips, Tools, and Techniques section.
4. **Get Extra Rest**
5. **Remember to Live Day-By-Day**

Until next time... LIVE INSPIRED!

"WITH EVERY RISING OF THE SUN, THINK OF YOUR LIFE AS JUST BEGUN..."

-ROBIN SHEA

GROUND YOUR DAY IN THESE POSITIVE PRACTICES...

DISCOVERY THROUGH JOURNALING

Catalyst Goal - "Shooting Star Goals"

LIST YOUR SHORT-TERM, FEEL-GOOD GOAL FOR THE DAY: _____

_____

_____

Process/Performance Visualization - "Preview of Success"

LIST 3 PROCESS AND/ OR PERFORMANCE STRUGGLES:

1. _____

2. _____

3. _____

LIST 3 WAYS YOU ENVISION YOURSELF OVERCOMING THESE 3 OBSTACLES:

1. _____

2. _____

3. _____

Projected Visualization - "Future Self Meditation"

LIST 3 "FUTURE SELF" SCENARIOS IN WHICH YOU ARE LIVING YOUR ENVISIONED LIFE.

1. _____

2. _____

3. _____

Expectations and Custom Goal Setting

☐   MY EXPECTATIONS ARE LINING UP WITH MY BELIEF SYSTEM.

LIST 3 "I AM" STATEMENTS:

1. _____

2. _____

3. _____

END YOUR DAY WITH THESE HELPFUL PRACTICES . . .

Reflection – "The Day's Lessons"

EVENT:

STUMBLE:

TOOL:

H.A.P.P.I.N.E.S.S. Victories

LIST 3 EMOTIONAL VICTORIES YOU ACHIEVED TODAY:

1.

2.

3.

NUTRITION

☐ I AM HONORING MY BODY BY HONORING THE GUIDELINES OF MY NUTRITIONAL PLAN.

FITNESS

☐ I AM HONORING MY BODY BY HONORING MY SELECTED FITNESS PLAN.

SUPPORT

☐ I AM RECEIVING SUPPORT

☐ I AM GIVING SUPPORT

LIST 3 PEOPLE YOU RECEIVE SUPPORT FROM OR PROVIDE SUPPORT TO:

1.

2.

3.

MY SUPPORT TEAM IS:

☐ SAFE

☐ EMPATHETIC

☐ SOLUTION-FOCUSED

This is my journey...

MY THOUGHTS DETERMINE WHO I AM,

WHAT I HAVE,

AND WHAT I CAN DO.

THE POWER TO DECIDE MY LIFE RESTS INSIDE OF ME

THROUGH THE HOLY SPIRIT AND I BOLDLY CLAIM

MY RIGHT TO LIVE WITH GRACE AND GLORY ON MY SIDE.

MY THOUGHTS WILL REFLECT A LOVE FOR MYSELF ONLY EQUALED

BY GOD'S LOVE FOR ME.

My mind is alert.

MY HEART IS OPEN AND JOY AND HAPPINESS ARE MY GUIDING LIGHTS.

AMEN.

DAILY BLESSINGS

Day Five: Phase Two

The average toddler hears "no," 400 times a day! Children who hear "no" too much have higher frustration levels, anxiety, and poor communication skills. In addition to this, children begin to tune "no" out completely.

We are "no" different (pardon the pun) than toddlers at this level of the transformation process. Saying "no" to an unwanted behavior will only leave us frustrated, raise our anxiety levels, and interfere with our productive self-talk. Break out of the "Yes"/"No" tug-of-war by filling your toolbox with skills that redirect behavior rather than slap it on the hand.

Explore these ideas and then come up with some of your own.

1. Say YES more often - Try rephrasing the "no" as a "yes". Say, "Yes, I can have that chocolate cake for my 20% Indulgent dish on Sunday. I'll pass on it for now."
2. Say NO less often - Reserve absolute no's only for behaviors with too much temptation. If you use "no" less often it becomes a more powerful self-regulating command. If something simply possesses too much temptation, or is too much of a gateway behavior, say "no" with authority to yourself.
3. Show and Tell - Maybe your behavior isn't as bad as you think! Show and Tell simply means analyze the behavior and try modifying it to fit into your new lifestyle.

Until next time, LIVE INSPIRED!

"WITH EVERY RISING OF THE SUN, THINK OF YOUR LIFE AS JUST BEGUN..."

-ROBIN SHEA

GROUND YOUR DAY IN THESE POSITIVE PRACTICES...

DISCOVERY THROUGH JOURNALING

Catalyst Goal - "Shooting Star Goals"

LIST YOUR SHORT-TERM, FEEL-GOOD GOAL FOR THE DAY:

_____

_____

Process/Performance Visualization - "Preview of Success"

LIST 3 PROCESS AND/OR PERFORMANCE STRUGGLES:

1. _____

2. _____

3. _____

LIST 3 WAYS YOU ENVISION YOURSELF OVERCOMING THESE 3 OBSTACLES:

1. _____

2. _____

3. _____

Projected Visualization - "Future Self Meditation"

LIST 3 "FUTURE SELF" SCENARIOS IN WHICH YOU ARE LIVING YOUR ENVISIONED LIFE.

1. _____

2. _____

3. _____

Expectations and Custom Goal Setting

☐ MY EXPECTATIONS ARE LINING UP WITH MY BELIEF SYSTEM.

LIST 3 "I AM" STATEMENTS:

1. _____

2. _____

3. _____

Reflection – "The Day's Lessons"

EVENT:_____

STUMBLE:_____

TOOL:_____

_____

_____

_____

_____

H.A.P.P.I.N.E.S.S. Victories

LIST 3 EMOTIONAL VICTORIES YOU ACHIEVED TODAY:

1. _____

2. _____

3. _____

NUTRITION

☐ I AM HONORING MY BODY BY HONORING THE GUIDELINES OF MY NUTRITIONAL PLAN.

FITNESS

☐ I AM HONORING MY BODY BY HONORING MY SELECTED FITNESS PLAN.

SUPPORT

☐ I AM RECEIVING SUPPORT

☐ I AM GIVING SUPPORT

LIST 3 PEOPLE YOU RECEIVE SUPPORT FROM OR PROVIDE SUPPORT TO:

1. _____

2. _____

3. _____

MY SUPPORT TEAM IS:

☐ SAFE

☐ EMPATHETIC

☐ SOLUTION-FOCUSED

This is my journey...

MY THOUGHTS DETERMINE WHO I AM,

WHAT I HAVE,

AND WHAT I CAN DO.

THE POWER TO DECIDE MY LIFE RESTS INSIDE OF ME

THROUGH THE HOLY SPIRIT AND I BOLDLY CLAIM

MY RIGHT TO LIVE WITH GRACE AND GLORY ON MY SIDE.

MY THOUGHTS WILL REFLECT A LOVE FOR MYSELF ONLY EQUALED

BY GOD'S LOVE FOR ME.

My mind is alert.

MY HEART IS OPEN AND JOY AND HAPPINESS ARE MY GUIDING LIGHTS.

AMEN.

DAILY BLESSINGS

Before the Fork

Day Six: Phase Two

When my son, Rowdy, works with horses, he is brilliant. He is patient, kind, thoughtful, intentional, deliberate and focused. Each training session has a purpose; the horse is corrected and redirected with a kind and gentle hand. There is no place for anger in the arena. Sure, repetition, allowance, correction, redirection, but no anger. When Rowdy begins getting frustrated, or his horse begins to become unresponsive to training, he backs off for the day and lets his mind (and the horse's mind) relax. Nothing good is accomplished through an angry, frustrated training session. Rowdy has loved working with horses his entire life, and his commitment to their wellbeing is paramount to everything he does. Rowdy has been (and continues to be) guided and trained by Master Trainer, Josh Lyons. Josh has passed down to Rowdy the proper care and training techniques that will allow Rowdy to get the most from his horses all while providing them an environment to thrive.

You will be filling both roles in your life: Master Trainer, and Horse. Every day you must care and love yourself with a gentle hand. Stretch yourself, but be forgiving, use repetition, correction, and redirection but NO ANGER. In the process, you will upgrade your decision-making skills, learn to deal with rejection or frustrations from a growth oriented perspective, and enjoy the process of each experience.

This requires a daily commitment of FOCUS and TIME through the Creation Mind (not the Survival Mind). Use questions that promote growth; these are problem-solving questions. The second you feel yourself getting frustrated with the process of expansion, back away, breathe, and relax into the accomplishments you have already made. Once your Survival Mind is activated, all of your negative emotions will start driving. Don't try and problem solve while angry, frustrated, or feeling any Red or Yellow Zone emotions. This is the primary requirement of success. You must invest the TIME to LEARN under the right mental conditions.

Until next time, LIVE INSPIRED!

"WITH EVERY RISING OF THE SUN, THINK OF YOUR LIFE AS JUST BEGUN..."

-ROBIN SHEA

GROUND YOUR DAY IN THESE POSITIVE PRACTICES...

DISCOVERY THROUGH JOURNALING

Catalyst Goal - "Shooting Star Goals"

LIST YOUR SHORT-TERM, FEEL-GOOD GOAL FOR THE DAY: _____

_____

_____

Process/Performance Visualization - "Preview of Success"

LIST 3 PROCESS AND/ OR PERFORMANCE STRUGGLES:

1. _____
2. _____
3. _____

LIST 3 WAYS YOU ENVISION YOURSELF OVERCOMING THESE 3 OBSTACLES:

1. _____
2. _____
3. _____

Projected Visualization - "Future Self Meditation"

LIST 3 "FUTURE SELF" SCENARIOS IN WHICH YOU ARE LIVING YOUR ENVISIONED LIFE.

1. _____
2. _____
3. _____

Expectations and Custom Goal Setting

☐ MY EXPECTATIONS ARE LINING UP WITH MY BELIEF SYSTEM.

LIST 3 "I AM" STATEMENTS:

1. _____
2. _____
3. _____

Reflection – "The Day's Lessons"

EVENT:_____

STUMBLE:_____

TOOL:_____

_____

_____

_____

_____

H.A.P.P.I.N.E.S.S. Victories

LIST 3 EMOTIONAL VICTORIES YOU ACHIEVED TODAY:

1. _____

2. _____

3. _____

NUTRITION

☐ I AM HONORING MY BODY BY HONORING THE GUIDELINES OF MY NUTRITIONAL PLAN.

FITNESS

☐ I AM HONORING MY BODY BY HONORING MY SELECTED FITNESS PLAN.

SUPPORT

☐ I AM RECEIVING SUPPORT

☐ I AM GIVING SUPPORT

LIST 3 PEOPLE YOU RECEIVE SUPPORT FROM OR PROVIDE SUPPORT TO:

1. _____

2. _____

3. _____

MY SUPPORT TEAM IS:

☐ SAFE

☐ EMPATHETIC

☐ SOLUTION-FOCUSED

This is my journey...

MY THOUGHTS DETERMINE WHO I AM,

WHAT I HAVE,

AND WHAT I CAN DO.

THE POWER TO DECIDE MY LIFE RESTS INSIDE OF ME

THROUGH THE HOLY SPIRIT AND I BOLDLY CLAIM

MY RIGHT TO LIVE WITH GRACE AND GLORY ON MY SIDE.

MY THOUGHTS WILL REFLECT A LOVE FOR MYSELF ONLY EQUALED

BY GOD'S LOVE FOR ME.

My mind is alert.

MY HEART IS OPEN AND JOY AND HAPPINESS ARE MY GUIDING LIGHTS.

AMEN.

DAILY BLESSINGS

Day Seven: Phase Two

The human body is naturally buoyant when the lungs are filled with air; therefore, if you take a deep breath, and relax into the chaos, you won't sink. Better yet, you will float! Relax, breathe, and let the current carry you.

To strengthen our new habits, we have to invite a variety of situations into our daily life. This is the only way we can build effective tools and exercise our new chosen behaviors. So many people choose to experience this process through struggle; gasping for air and fighting to keep their heads above water.

The key to a successful transformation is when you joyfully play in the current of change but understand that when you become tired, it's time to relax into the current.

I will be driving this point home over the next couple of weeks. Don't struggle with the process, relax into the discomfort with curiosity. Remember the Road to Change, the path you chose to take? Well, I warned you it would feel like a wasteland, and you should be understanding that about now. But don't turn around and run home to familiar — stay the course and develop skills, one obstacle at a time. And when you are feeling weary, rest into the current and let it carry you.

Until next time, LIVE INSPIRED!

"WITH EVERY RISING OF THE SUN, THINK OF YOUR LIFE AS JUST BEGUN..."

-ROBIN SHEA

GROUND YOUR DAY IN THESE POSITIVE PRACTICES...

DISCOVERY THROUGH JOURNALING

Catalyst Goal - "Shooting Star Goals"

LIST YOUR SHORT-TERM, FEEL-GOOD GOAL FOR THE DAY: _____

_____

_____

Process/Performance Visualization - "Preview of Success"

LIST 3 PROCESS AND/OR PERFORMANCE STRUGGLES:

1. _____
2. _____
3. _____

LIST 3 WAYS YOU ENVISION YOURSELF OVERCOMING THESE 3 OBSTACLES:

1. _____
2. _____
3. _____

Projected Visualization - "Future Self Meditation"

LIST 3 "FUTURE SELF" SCENARIOS IN WHICH YOU ARE LIVING YOUR ENVISIONED LIFE.

1. _____
2. _____
3. _____

Expectations and Custom Goal Setting

☐   MY EXPECTATIONS ARE LINING UP WITH MY BELIEF SYSTEM.

LIST 3 "I AM" STATEMENTS:

1. _____
2. _____
3. _____

Reflection – "The Day's Lessons"

EVENT:_____

STUMBLE:_____

TOOL:_____

_____

_____

_____

_____

H.A.P.P.I.N.E.S.S. Victories

LIST 3 EMOTIONAL VICTORIES YOU ACHIEVED TODAY:

1. _____

2. _____

3. _____

NUTRITION

☐ I AM HONORING MY BODY BY HONORING THE GUIDELINES OF MY NUTRITIONAL PLAN.

FITNESS

☐ I AM HONORING MY BODY BY HONORING MY SELECTED FITNESS PLAN.

SUPPORT

☐ I AM RECEIVING SUPPORT

☐ I AM GIVING SUPPORT

LIST 3 PEOPLE YOU RECEIVE SUPPORT FROM OR PROVIDE SUPPORT TO:

1. _____

2. _____

3. _____

MY SUPPORT TEAM IS:

☐ SAFE

☐ EMPATHETIC

☐ SOLUTION-FOCUSED

This is my journey...

MY THOUGHTS DETERMINE WHO I AM,

WHAT I HAVE,

AND WHAT I CAN DO.

THE POWER TO DECIDE MY LIFE RESTS INSIDE OF ME

THROUGH THE HOLY SPIRIT AND I BOLDLY CLAIM

MY RIGHT TO LIVE WITH GRACE AND GLORY ON MY SIDE.

MY THOUGHTS WILL REFLECT A LOVE FOR MYSELF ONLY EQUALED

BY GOD'S LOVE FOR ME.

My mind is alert.

MY HEART IS OPEN AND JOY AND HAPPINESS ARE MY GUIDING LIGHTS.

AMEN.

DAILY BLESSINGS

Day Eight: Phase Two

Two of the most underutilized words in healthy lifestyle transformation: REST and REPAIR.

You are an infant in the transformation process; you will require the same love and care to grow and thrive. But, unlike an infant, you have the power to assume each role in your life that is so critical to your success.

Be the CREATOR that paints a vivid and palpable vision of the future.
Be the Father that protects the vision with a fierce and unwavering strength.
Be the Mother that prepares for the vision with care and diligence.
Be the Baby that requires rest and care to realize the vision.

Until next time, LIVE INSPIRED!

"WITH EVERY RISING OF THE SUN, THINK OF YOUR LIFE AS JUST BEGUN..."

-ROBIN SHEA

GROUND YOUR DAY IN THESE POSITIVE PRACTICES...

DISCOVERY THROUGH JOURNALING

Catalyst Goal - "Shooting Star Goals"

LIST YOUR SHORT-TERM, FEEL-GOOD GOAL FOR THE DAY: _____

_____

_____

Process/Performance Visualization - "Preview of Success"

LIST 3 PROCESS AND/OR PERFORMANCE STRUGGLES:

1. _____
2. _____
3. _____

LIST 3 WAYS YOU ENVISION YOURSELF OVERCOMING THESE 3 OBSTACLES:

1. _____
2. _____
3. _____

Projected Visualization - "Future Self Meditation"

LIST 3 "FUTURE SELF" SCENARIOS IN WHICH YOU ARE LIVING YOUR ENVISIONED LIFE.

1. _____
2. _____
3. _____

Expectations and Custom Goal Setting

☐ MY EXPECTATIONS ARE LINING UP WITH MY BELIEF SYSTEM.

LIST 3 "I AM" STATEMENTS:

1. _____
2. _____
3. _____

Reflection – "The Day's Lessons"

EVENT:—————————————————————————

STUMBLE:—————————————————————————

TOOL:—————————————————————————

H.A.P.P.I.N.E.S.S. Victories

LIST 3 EMOTIONAL VICTORIES YOU ACHIEVED TODAY:

1. _____

2. _____

3. _____

NUTRITION

☐ I AM HONORING MY BODY BY HONORING THE GUIDELINES OF MY NUTRITIONAL PLAN.

FITNESS

☐ I AM HONORING MY BODY BY HONORING MY SELECTED FITNESS PLAN.

SUPPORT

☐ I AM RECEIVING SUPPORT

☐ I AM GIVING SUPPORT

LIST 3 PEOPLE YOU RECEIVE SUPPORT FROM OR PROVIDE SUPPORT TO:

1. _____

2. _____

3. _____

MY SUPPORT TEAM IS:

☐ SAFE

☐ EMPATHETIC

☐ SOLUTION-FOCUSED

This is my journey...

MY THOUGHTS DETERMINE WHO I AM,

WHAT I HAVE,

AND WHAT I CAN DO.

THE POWER TO DECIDE MY LIFE RESTS INSIDE OF ME

THROUGH THE HOLY SPIRIT AND I BOLDLY CLAIM

MY RIGHT TO LIVE WITH GRACE AND GLORY ON MY SIDE.

MY THOUGHTS WILL REFLECT A LOVE FOR MYSELF ONLY EQUALED

BY GOD'S LOVE FOR ME.

My mind is alert.

MY HEART IS OPEN AND JOY AND HAPPINESS ARE MY GUIDING LIGHTS.

AMEN.

DAILY BLESSINGS

Day Nine: Phase Two

When your life begins to take shape, just as you have envisioned, you can expect a series of three reactions from your family and friends.

They will first notice that something is different about you. They may not be able to pinpoint the change, but they will sense your positive energy. Next, they will begin asking questions to determine if your transformation would be suitable for them. Finally, they will ask for your guidance in redirecting their life.

If you remember, my Why Story is:

I Pay JOY and HAPPINESS Forward
I teach people to reinvent their relationship with food through alignment with JOY and HAPPINESS, paying forward what was gifted to me.

Sharing your transformation reinforces everything you have learned and is a valuable tool in strengthening your new neural connections.

Too soon? That's okay. Don't rush the process; you will know when the time is right to share your transformation. Sharing is such a valuable part of the process, so be open to signs.

Until next time, LIVE INSPIRED!

"WITH EVERY RISING OF THE SUN, THINK OF YOUR LIFE AS JUST BEGUN..."

-ROBIN SHEA

GROUND YOUR DAY IN THESE POSITIVE PRACTICES...

DISCOVERY THROUGH JOURNALING

Catalyst Goal - "Shooting Star Goals"

LIST YOUR SHORT-TERM, FEEL-GOOD GOAL FOR THE DAY: _____

_____

_____

Process/Performance Visualization - "Preview of Success"

LIST 3 PROCESS AND/OR PERFORMANCE STRUGGLES:

1. _____
2. _____
3. _____

LIST 3 WAYS YOU ENVISION YOURSELF OVERCOMING THESE 3 OBSTACLES:

1. _____
2. _____
3. _____

Projected Visualization - "Future Self Meditation"

LIST 3 "FUTURE SELF" SCENARIOS IN WHICH YOU ARE LIVING YOUR ENVISIONED LIFE.

1. _____
2. _____
3. _____

Expectations and Custom Goal Setting

☐ MY EXPECTATIONS ARE LINING UP WITH MY BELIEF SYSTEM.

LIST 3 "I AM" STATEMENTS:

1. _____
2. _____
3. _____

Reflection – "The Day's Lessons"

EVENT:—————————————————————

STUMBLE:—————————————————————

TOOL:—————————————————————

H.A.P.P.I.N.E.S.S. Victories

LIST 3 EMOTIONAL VICTORIES YOU ACHIEVED TODAY:

1. —————————————————————
2. —————————————————————
3. —————————————————————

NUTRITION

☐ I AM HONORING MY BODY BY HONORING THE GUIDELINES OF MY NUTRITIONAL PLAN.

FITNESS

☐ I AM HONORING MY BODY BY HONORING MY SELECTED FITNESS PLAN.

SUPPORT

☐ I AM RECEIVING SUPPORT

☐ I AM GIVING SUPPORT

LIST 3 PEOPLE YOU RECEIVE SUPPORT FROM OR PROVIDE SUPPORT TO:

1. —————————————————————
2. —————————————————————
3. —————————————————————

MY SUPPORT TEAM IS:

☐ SAFE

☐ EMPATHETIC

☐ SOLUTION-FOCUSED

This is my journey...

MY THOUGHTS DETERMINE WHO I AM,

WHAT I HAVE,

AND WHAT I CAN DO.

THE POWER TO DECIDE MY LIFE RESTS INSIDE OF ME

THROUGH THE HOLY SPIRIT AND I BOLDLY CLAIM

MY RIGHT TO LIVE WITH GRACE AND GLORY ON MY SIDE.

MY THOUGHTS WILL REFLECT A LOVE FOR MYSELF ONLY EQUALED

BY GOD'S LOVE FOR ME.

My mind is alert.

MY HEART IS OPEN AND JOY AND HAPPINESS ARE MY GUIDING LIGHTS.

AMEN.

DAILY BLESSINGS

Day Ten: Phase Two

You can face anything in front of you because of what is inside you. You are ten days into the process of transformation. Not only is your world being rocked, but the ones that love you the most are left wondering, "What the heck is going on?" They love you as you are, and your transformation is making them extremely uncomfortable. Before you get angry and go to battle with your loved ones, just remember this: Their fear is born of love.

Your loved ones provide some of the greatest growth opportunities you will encounter. They know your hot buttons, your favorite foods, how to use guilt against you, and they are comfortable and familiar. They love you despite your desire to grow. Here are some tips that will allow you to grow while preserving relationships and disarming opposition.

This is H.A.P.P.I.N.E.S.S. Ladder work at its finest. The first thing to do is recognize the enemy is not your relative but a few emotions your relative may be experiencing. Address these emotions through love and acceptance, and you will be honoring your relationships.

1. **Ignorance:** Such a hard word, and one I am not very comfortable using, but it is the right word. Your opposition is ignorant to your Why Story.
2. **Unbelief:** No one taught your opposition how to dream, but it is never too late. You can be the "game changer" in their life just by sharing your Why Story with them. Once they see you succeed, they may have the confidence to build their own Why Story.
3. **Fear:** Your opposition is afraid. They are afraid they will lose you, or your success will diminish them in some way. Look for opportunities to strengthen your relationship with them outside of your differences. For example, if you no longer share the same food world, find another activity you enjoy doing together and build off of that.

The only defense you have to disarm your opposition and honor your love for them is through unconditional love, no expectations, and faith. Believe in your Why Story, and through your actions and commitment, you may empower them to remove their roadblocks and begin seeking understanding, belief, and faith.

Until next time, LIVE INSPIRED!

"WITH EVERY RISING OF THE SUN, THINK OF YOUR LIFE AS JUST BEGUN..."

-ROBIN SHEA

GROUND YOUR DAY IN THESE POSITIVE PRACTICES...

DISCOVERY THROUGH JOURNALING

Catalyst Goal - "Shooting Star Goals"

LIST YOUR SHORT-TERM, FEEL-GOOD GOAL FOR THE DAY: _____

_____

_____

Process/Performance Visualization - "Preview of Success"

LIST 3 PROCESS AND/OR PERFORMANCE STRUGGLES:

1. _____

2. _____

3. _____

LIST 3 WAYS YOU ENVISION YOURSELF OVERCOMING THESE 3 OBSTACLES:

1. _____

2. _____

3. _____

Projected Visualization - "Future Self Meditation"

LIST 3 "FUTURE SELF" SCENARIOS IN WHICH YOU ARE LIVING YOUR ENVISIONED LIFE.

1. _____

2. _____

3. _____

Expectations and Custom Goal Setting

☐ MY EXPECTATIONS ARE LINING UP WITH MY BELIEF SYSTEM.

LIST 3 "I AM" STATEMENTS:

1. _____

2. _____

3. _____

END YOUR DAY WITH THESE HELPFUL PRACTICES...

Reflection – "The Day's Lessons"

EVENT:_____

STUMBLE:_____

TOOL:_____

_____

_____

_____

_____

H.A.P.P.I.N.E.S.S. Victories

LIST 3 EMOTIONAL VICTORIES YOU ACHIEVED TODAY:

1. _____
2. _____
3. _____

NUTRITION

☐ I AM HONORING MY BODY BY HONORING THE GUIDELINES OF MY NUTRITIONAL PLAN.

FITNESS

☐ I AM HONORING MY BODY BY HONORING MY SELECTED FITNESS PLAN.

SUPPORT

☐ I AM RECEIVING SUPPORT

☐ I AM GIVING SUPPORT

LIST 3 PEOPLE YOU RECEIVE SUPPORT FROM OR PROVIDE SUPPORT TO:

1. _____
2. _____
3. _____

MY SUPPORT TEAM IS:

☐ SAFE

☐ EMPATHETIC

☐ SOLUTION-FOCUSED

This is my journey...

MY THOUGHTS DETERMINE WHO I AM,

WHAT I HAVE,

AND WHAT I CAN DO.

THE POWER TO DECIDE MY LIFE RESTS INSIDE OF ME

THROUGH THE HOLY SPIRIT AND I BOLDLY CLAIM

MY RIGHT TO LIVE WITH GRACE AND GLORY ON MY SIDE.

MY THOUGHTS WILL REFLECT A LOVE FOR MYSELF ONLY EQUALED

BY GOD'S LOVE FOR ME.

My mind is alert.

MY HEART IS OPEN AND JOY AND HAPPINESS ARE MY GUIDING LIGHTS.

AMEN.

DAILY BLESSINGS

Day Eleven: Phase Two

Why do some people refuse to embrace change regardless of how dire the situation is? They keep eating junk, keep smoking, and continue to drink and more—even after the doctor pleads for a lifestyle change. Why are they stuck?

That's the WRONG question.

Rather than ask, "Why Won't They Embrace Change?" let's ask, "Why Do People Break Through?"

When fear shifts from, "What if I fail?" to "What would life be like if I follow through?" you are on the verge of a breakthrough.

Being inspired to live life to the fullest through a deep connection to your Desired Self, despite setbacks, is much more powerful than being afraid of failure and never trying.

It's much like the phrase, "Burn the boat and storm the shore." You do what it takes to move forward into your potential, without the chance of retreating into old sabotaging habits. You raise your standards!

What was acceptable yesterday is no longer acceptable today. You will rise and meet your standards, and your needs. So, if your standards are lower than you would like, and you do not perceive your transformation as a "need," you will struggle much more during your transformation.

BURN THE BOATS AND STORM THE SHORE. It is the only way to ensure you do not fall back into a life of complacency and disregard for potential.

Until next time, LIVE INSPIRED!

"WITH EVERY RISING OF THE SUN, THINK OF YOUR LIFE AS JUST BEGUN..."

-ROBIN SHEA

GROUND YOUR DAY IN THESE POSITIVE PRACTICES...

DISCOVERY THROUGH JOURNALING

Catalyst Goal - "Shooting Star Goals"

LIST YOUR SHORT-TERM, FEEL-GOOD GOAL FOR THE DAY: _____

_____

_____

Process/Performance Visualization - "Preview of Success"

LIST 3 PROCESS AND/ OR PERFORMANCE STRUGGLES:

1. _____

2. _____

3. _____

LIST 3 WAYS YOU ENVISION YOURSELF OVERCOMING THESE 3 OBSTACLES:

1. _____

2. _____

3. _____

Projected Visualization - "Future Self Meditation"

LIST 3 "FUTURE SELF" SCENARIOS IN WHICH YOU ARE LIVING YOUR ENVISIONED LIFE.

1. _____

2. _____

3. _____

Expectations and Custom Goal Setting

☐ MY EXPECTATIONS ARE LINING UP WITH MY BELIEF SYSTEM.

LIST 3 "I AM" STATEMENTS:

1. _____

2. _____

3. _____

Reflection – "The Day's Lessons"

EVENT:

STUMBLE:

TOOL:

H.A.P.P.I.N.E.S.S. Victories

LIST 3 EMOTIONAL VICTORIES YOU ACHIEVED TODAY:

1.

2.

3.

NUTRITION

☐ I AM HONORING MY BODY BY HONORING THE GUIDELINES OF MY NUTRITIONAL PLAN.

FITNESS

☐ I AM HONORING MY BODY BY HONORING MY SELECTED FITNESS PLAN.

SUPPORT

☐ I AM RECEIVING SUPPORT

☐ I AM GIVING SUPPORT

LIST 3 PEOPLE YOU RECEIVE SUPPORT FROM OR PROVIDE SUPPORT TO:

1.

2.

3.

MY SUPPORT TEAM IS:

☐ SAFE

☐ EMPATHETIC

☐ SOLUTION-FOCUSED

This is my journey...

MY THOUGHTS DETERMINE WHO I AM,

WHAT I HAVE,

AND WHAT I CAN DO.

THE POWER TO DECIDE MY LIFE RESTS INSIDE OF ME

THROUGH THE HOLY SPIRIT AND I BOLDLY CLAIM

MY RIGHT TO LIVE WITH GRACE AND GLORY ON MY SIDE.

MY THOUGHTS WILL REFLECT A LOVE FOR MYSELF ONLY EQUALED

BY GOD'S LOVE FOR ME.

My mind is alert.

MY HEART IS OPEN AND JOY AND HAPPINESS ARE MY GUIDING LIGHTS.

AMEN.

DAILY BLESSINGS

Before the Fork

Day Twelve: Phase Two

Fight or Flight — we've all heard the term, but do you fully grasp the importance of controlling your autonomic nervous system's response to perceived threats? Long story short (and without all the medical verbiage — well, at least toned down):

When we live our life using the Survival Mind, we activate our internal stress response system (Fight or Flight). Although this system serves a purpose in a life-threatening situation, we most often activate it in non life-threatening situations.

When the system is activated, blood is shunted out of the viscera (abdomen) and into the extremities (arms and legs) to enable us to react quickly to a life-threatening situation. Not only does the response redistribute blood in our body for movement, but it also shunts blood out of our forebrain (Creation) and into our hindbrain (Survival). This means we lose intelligence when we are under stress, and our forebrain's ability to guide our decision-making is severely impaired, if not disabled altogether.

All of the above would be necessary if a lion, tiger, or bear was chasing us. But, in the modern day, our fight-or-flight response is activated over only perceived threats (bills, weight gain, job, missed flight, people, strangers, children, relationships, etc.) and not life-threatening situations.

Our primal nervous system was designed to move effortlessly between our operating systems, one being Fight or Flight (sympathetic nervous system) and the other being Rest and Digest (parasympathetic nervous system). However, our modern environment is made of perceived threats in every direction, and as a result, our sympathetic nervous system (Fight or Flight) gets locked in the "on" position. This is known as Chronic Stress and the effects are devastating:

- **Physical:** Body's ability to heal and repair itself is inhibited.
- **Mental:** Blood is shunted from prefrontal cortex, which impairs conscious response.
- **Spiritual:** Stress activates low vibration thoughts which impair your ability to identify with your Why Story

Meditation has been proving very effective in deactivating Fight or Flight. Begin with a five-minute practice as outlined in State of Being Practices.

Until next time, LIVE INSPIRED!

"WITH EVERY RISING OF THE SUN, THINK OF YOUR LIFE AS JUST BEGUN..."

-ROBIN SHEA

GROUND YOUR DAY IN THESE POSITIVE PRACTICES...

DISCOVERY THROUGH JOURNALING

Catalyst Goal - "Shooting Star Goals"

LIST YOUR SHORT-TERM, FEEL-GOOD GOAL FOR THE DAY: _____

_____

_____

Process/Performance Visualization - "Preview of Success"

LIST 3 PROCESS AND/OR PERFORMANCE STRUGGLES:

1. _____
2. _____
3. _____

LIST 3 WAYS YOU ENVISION YOURSELF OVERCOMING THESE 3 OBSTACLES:

1. _____
2. _____
3. _____

Projected Visualization - "Future Self Meditation"

LIST 3 "FUTURE SELF" SCENARIOS IN WHICH YOU ARE LIVING YOUR ENVISIONED LIFE.

1. _____
2. _____
3. _____

Expectations and Custom Goal Setting

☐ MY EXPECTATIONS ARE LINING UP WITH MY BELIEF SYSTEM.

LIST 3 "I AM" STATEMENTS:

1. _____
2. _____
3. _____

Reflection – "The Day's Lessons"

EVENT:

STUMBLE:

TOOL:

H.A.P.P.I.N.E.S.S. Victories

LIST 3 EMOTIONAL VICTORIES YOU ACHIEVED TODAY:

1.

2.

3.

NUTRITION

☐ I AM HONORING MY BODY BY HONORING THE GUIDELINES OF MY NUTRITIONAL PLAN.

FITNESS

☐ I AM HONORING MY BODY BY HONORING MY SELECTED FITNESS PLAN.

SUPPORT

☐ I AM RECEIVING SUPPORT

☐ I AM GIVING SUPPORT

LIST 3 PEOPLE YOU RECEIVE SUPPORT FROM OR PROVIDE SUPPORT TO:

1.

2.

3.

MY SUPPORT TEAM IS:

☐ SAFE

☐ EMPATHETIC

☐ SOLUTION-FOCUSED

This is my journey...

MY THOUGHTS DETERMINE WHO I AM,

WHAT I HAVE,

AND WHAT I CAN DO.

THE POWER TO DECIDE MY LIFE RESTS INSIDE OF ME

THROUGH THE HOLY SPIRIT AND I BOLDLY CLAIM

MY RIGHT TO LIVE WITH GRACE AND GLORY ON MY SIDE.

MY THOUGHTS WILL REFLECT A LOVE FOR MYSELF ONLY EQUALED

BY GOD'S LOVE FOR ME.

My mind is alert.

MY HEART IS OPEN AND JOY AND HAPPINESS ARE MY GUIDING LIGHTS.

AMEN.

DAILY BLESSINGS

Day Thirteen: Phase Two

98% of dieters fail...OUCH! They either quit or are not able to keep the weight off permanently. This is because diets are too restrictive, eliminate needed food groups, are too low carb, too low fat, or just completely ridiculous!

There are BILLIONS of dollars being spent every year by hopefuls looking for the answer to their health and fitness woes. The 98% failure rate is never the focus of the industry, only the 2%. You and I are being sold on the 2% that find success!

Here is a great example:
Most gyms oversell their memberships by a minimum of 1,000%. That means that even though the gym can only accommodate 100 people at any given time, they have sold memberships to 1,000 people. Even if you divide the hours in a day by the number of people the gym can feasibly accommodate, the sad fact remains that the gym is counting on you not showing up.

I understand that businesses have to keep the lights on, but this business model concerns me because your failure is factored into to their success. It makes me scratch my head.

In my Pollyanna approach to life, I would like to think that every health and fitness professional is in this industry to make a difference in the lives of their clients; and although this business formula doesn't resonate well with my heart, I do have a certain degree of understanding.

You see, the answer to success lies in the 2%, plain and simple. I can study the 98% for a decade, and all I will find out is more ways to fail. But, by focusing on the 2%, I can identify and map their success formula. What switched on in the minds of the 2%? What behaviors, thought patterns, or spiritual awakenings took place to activate their Creative Mind? What made them accept a new lifestyle and transform their life? By focusing on the 2%, I am better equipped to guide the 98%. Make sense?

Study what is working in your transformation, not on what is not working. Build on your successes and forget your failures. You are the 2%, and your WINS have a lot to teach you about yourself.

Until next time, LIVE INSPIRED!

"WITH EVERY RISING OF THE SUN, THINK OF YOUR LIFE AS JUST BEGUN..."

-ROBIN SHEA

GROUND YOUR DAY IN THESE POSITIVE PRACTICES...

DISCOVERY THROUGH JOURNALING

Catalyst Goal - "Shooting Star Goals"

LIST YOUR SHORT-TERM, FEEL-GOOD GOAL FOR THE DAY: _____

_____

_____

Process/Performance Visualization - "Preview of Success"

LIST 3 PROCESS AND/ OR PERFORMANCE STRUGGLES:

1. _____
2. _____
3. _____

LIST 3 WAYS YOU ENVISION YOURSELF OVERCOMING THESE 3 OBSTACLES:

1. _____
2. _____
3. _____

Projected Visualization - "Future Self Meditation"

LIST 3 "FUTURE SELF" SCENARIOS IN WHICH YOU ARE LIVING YOUR ENVISIONED LIFE.

1. _____
2. _____
3. _____

Expectations and Custom Goal Setting

☐ MY EXPECTATIONS ARE LINING UP WITH MY BELIEF SYSTEM.

LIST 3 "I AM" STATEMENTS:

1. _____
2. _____
3. _____

Reflection – "The Day's Lessons"

EVENT:

STUMBLE:

TOOL:

H.A.P.P.I.N.E.S.S. Victories

LIST 3 EMOTIONAL VICTORIES YOU ACHIEVED TODAY:

1.

2.

3.

NUTRITION

☐ I AM HONORING MY BODY BY HONORING THE GUIDELINES OF MY NUTRITIONAL PLAN.

FITNESS

☐ I AM HONORING MY BODY BY HONORING MY SELECTED FITNESS PLAN.

SUPPORT

☐ I AM RECEIVING SUPPORT

☐ I AM GIVING SUPPORT

LIST 3 PEOPLE YOU RECEIVE SUPPORT FROM OR PROVIDE SUPPORT TO:

1.

2.

3.

MY SUPPORT TEAM IS:

☐ SAFE

☐ EMPATHETIC

☐ SOLUTION-FOCUSED

This is my journey...

MY THOUGHTS DETERMINE WHO I AM,

WHAT I HAVE,

AND WHAT I CAN DO.

THE POWER TO DECIDE MY LIFE RESTS INSIDE OF ME

THROUGH THE HOLY SPIRIT AND I BOLDLY CLAIM

MY RIGHT TO LIVE WITH GRACE AND GLORY ON MY SIDE.

MY THOUGHTS WILL REFLECT A LOVE FOR MYSELF ONLY EQUALED

BY GOD'S LOVE FOR ME.

My mind is alert.

MY HEART IS OPEN AND JOY AND HAPPINESS ARE MY GUIDING LIGHTS.

AMEN.

DAILY BLESSINGS

Day Fourteen: Phase Two

An expert beginner gets stuck in the knowledge of what to do. They know everything about the process to achieve success, yet they are unwilling to execute the steps to move their knowledge into new behavior.

You can read 100 books on how to ride a bike and highly educate the conscious mind on the principles, but until you actually sit on the bike, find your balance, pedal, make imbalance corrections, slow down, speed up, stop and start again, etc. you are only living in theory, and living in theory does not change behavior.

The conscious mind (our Creative Mind) can be highly educated, but permanent lifestyle change only happens when we practice new desired behaviors.

Practice, practice, practice... The process of transformation begins when we commit to the practice required to form new behaviors and reprogram our new "chosen" default behaviors.

Until next time, LIVE INSPIRED!

"WITH EVERY RISING OF THE SUN, THINK OF YOUR LIFE AS JUST BEGUN..."

-ROBIN SHEA

GROUND YOUR DAY IN THESE POSITIVE PRACTICES...

DISCOVERY THROUGH JOURNALING

Catalyst Goal - "Shooting Star Goals"

LIST YOUR SHORT-TERM, FEEL-GOOD GOAL FOR THE DAY: _____

_____

_____

Process/Performance Visualization - "Preview of Success"

LIST 3 PROCESS AND/OR PERFORMANCE STRUGGLES:

1. _____
2. _____
3. _____

LIST 3 WAYS YOU ENVISION YOURSELF OVERCOMING THESE 3 OBSTACLES:

1. _____
2. _____
3. _____

Projected Visualization - "Future Self Meditation"

LIST 3 "FUTURE SELF" SCENARIOS IN WHICH YOU ARE LIVING YOUR ENVISIONED LIFE.

1. _____
2. _____
3. _____

Expectations and Custom Goal Setting

☐ MY EXPECTATIONS ARE LINING UP WITH MY BELIEF SYSTEM.

LIST 3 "I AM" STATEMENTS:

1. _____
2. _____
3. _____

END YOUR DAY WITH THESE HELPFUL PRACTICES . . .

Reflection – "The Day's Lessons"

EVENT: _____

STUMBLE: _____

TOOL: _____

_____
_____
_____
_____
_____

H.A.P.P.I.N.E.S.S. Victories

LIST 3 EMOTIONAL VICTORIES YOU ACHIEVED TODAY:

1. _____
2. _____
3. _____

NUTRITION

☐ I AM HONORING MY BODY BY HONORING THE GUIDELINES OF MY NUTRITIONAL PLAN.

FITNESS

☐ I AM HONORING MY BODY BY HONORING MY SELECTED FITNESS PLAN.

SUPPORT

☐ I AM RECEIVING SUPPORT

☐ I AM GIVING SUPPORT

LIST 3 PEOPLE YOU RECEIVE SUPPORT FROM OR PROVIDE SUPPORT TO:

1. _____
2. _____
3. _____

MY SUPPORT TEAM IS:

☐ SAFE

☐ EMPATHETIC

☐ SOLUTION-FOCUSED

This is my journey...

MY THOUGHTS DETERMINE WHO I AM,

WHAT I HAVE,

AND WHAT I CAN DO.

THE POWER TO DECIDE MY LIFE RESTS INSIDE OF ME

THROUGH THE HOLY SPIRIT AND I BOLDLY CLAIM

MY RIGHT TO LIVE WITH GRACE AND GLORY ON MY SIDE.

MY THOUGHTS WILL REFLECT A LOVE FOR MYSELF ONLY EQUALED

BY GOD'S LOVE FOR ME.

My mind is alert.

MY HEART IS OPEN AND JOY AND HAPPINESS ARE MY GUIDING LIGHTS.

AMEN.

DAILY BLESSINGS

Day Fifteen: Phase Two

Creating a "Time Budget" is telling your life (and everyone in it) what's happening next, instead of wondering why you can't fit it all in.

Time runs a very close parallel to money. Some people squander their money and wonder why they are broke, and others squander their time and wonder why they can't achieve their dreams. Either way, it is a budgeting issue!

When you approach your day with intention, people tend to get out of your way. When you approach your day with no intention, people tend to fill it with their own.

You must spend your time *before you spend your time*. Pair up activities, breathe more intention into your day, and make each moment count.

The one commodity we each share is the same 24 hours in every day. No one gets more time than another, yet some squeeze a week into a single 24-hour block. These people live with intention, never leaving a minute to chance (unless chance is factored into their day).

Look for the opportunity to squeeze more LIFE out of your 24-hour GIFT. You'll be surprised how much life you've been wasting with an inefficient "Time Budget." A great tool for this is using 250/250 or 1*2*3* Magic, which you will find in the next section. Get your workout in and ramp up your nutrition effortlessly just by shifting into the opportunity mindset.

Until next time, LIVE INSPIRED!

"WITH EVERY RISING OF THE SUN, THINK OF YOUR LIFE AS JUST BEGUN..."

-ROBIN SHEA

GROUND YOUR DAY IN THESE POSITIVE PRACTICES...

DISCOVERY THROUGH JOURNALING

Catalyst Goal - "Shooting Star Goals"

LIST YOUR SHORT-TERM, FEEL-GOOD GOAL FOR THE DAY: _____

_____

_____

Process/Performance Visualization - "Preview of Success"

LIST 3 PROCESS AND/OR PERFORMANCE STRUGGLES:

1. _____
2. _____
3. _____

LIST 3 WAYS YOU ENVISION YOURSELF OVERCOMING THESE 3 OBSTACLES:

1. _____
2. _____
3. _____

Projected Visualization - "Future Self Meditation"

LIST 3 "FUTURE SELF" SCENARIOS IN WHICH YOU ARE LIVING YOUR ENVISIONED LIFE.

1. _____
2. _____
3. _____

Expectations and Custom Goal Setting

☐ MY EXPECTATIONS ARE LINING UP WITH MY BELIEF SYSTEM.

LIST 3 "I AM" STATEMENTS:

1. _____
2. _____
3. _____

Reflection – "The Day's Lessons"

EVENT:————————————————————————————

STUMBLE:————————————————————————————

TOOL:————————————————————————————

————————————————————————————————

————————————————————————————————

————————————————————————————————

————————————————————————————————

H.A.P.P.I.N.E.S.S. Victories

LIST 3 EMOTIONAL VICTORIES YOU ACHIEVED TODAY:

1. ————————————————————————————

2. ————————————————————————————

3. ————————————————————————————

NUTRITION

☐ I AM HONORING MY BODY BY HONORING THE GUIDELINES OF MY NUTRITIONAL PLAN.

FITNESS

☐ I AM HONORING MY BODY BY HONORING MY SELECTED FITNESS PLAN.

SUPPORT

☐ I AM RECEIVING SUPPORT

☐ I AM GIVING SUPPORT

LIST 3 PEOPLE YOU RECEIVE SUPPORT FROM OR PROVIDE SUPPORT TO:

1. ————————————————————————————

2. ————————————————————————————

3. ————————————————————————————

MY SUPPORT TEAM IS:

☐ SAFE

☐ EMPATHETIC

☐ SOLUTION-FOCUSED

This is my journey...

MY THOUGHTS DETERMINE WHO I AM,

WHAT I HAVE,

AND WHAT I CAN DO.

THE POWER TO DECIDE MY LIFE RESTS INSIDE OF ME

THROUGH THE HOLY SPIRIT AND I BOLDLY CLAIM

MY RIGHT TO LIVE WITH GRACE AND GLORY ON MY SIDE.

MY THOUGHTS WILL REFLECT A LOVE FOR MYSELF ONLY EQUALED

BY GOD'S LOVE FOR ME.

My mind is alert.

MY HEART IS OPEN AND JOY AND HAPPINESS ARE MY GUIDING LIGHTS.

AMEN.

DAILY BLESSINGS

Day Sixteen: Phase Two

A Dreamer's Gotta Dream and a Planner's Gotta Plan...

We all know someone who wastes their days so deeply engrossed in the "IDEA" of something, but never commits to the steps necessary to make their dream a reality. On the flip side, we all know someone who plans too much for the future and ends up missing out on life altogether.

Remember when I told you about the Architect and the Dreamer? What if you could join the Architect and the Dreamer, the Vacationer and the Travel Agent, the Party Planner and the Guest of Honor? This union would result in one fantastic life.

The simple technique of Super Brain Yoga, which you will find in the next section, is one of the many tools that can help you blend these two opposing sides of your thinking.

No one side is better than the other because alone they are both imbalanced, but joining them creates a cohesiveness that will GET THINGS DONE, and sets you up to enjoy life on an entirely new level.

Give it a try!

Until next time, LIVE INSPIRED!

"WITH EVERY RISING OF THE SUN, THINK OF YOUR LIFE AS JUST BEGUN . . ."

-ROBIN SHEA

GROUND YOUR DAY IN THESE POSITIVE PRACTICES . . .

DISCOVERY THROUGH JOURNALING

Catalyst Goal - "Shooting Star Goals"

LIST YOUR SHORT-TERM, FEEL-GOOD GOAL FOR THE DAY: _____

_____

_____

Process/Performance Visualization - "Preview of Success"

LIST 3 PROCESS AND/OR PERFORMANCE STRUGGLES:

1. _____
2. _____
3. _____

LIST 3 WAYS YOU ENVISION YOURSELF OVERCOMING THESE 3 OBSTACLES:

1. _____
2. _____
3. _____

Projected Visualization - "Future Self Meditation"

LIST 3 "FUTURE SELF" SCENARIOS IN WHICH YOU ARE LIVING YOUR ENVISIONED LIFE.

1. _____
2. _____
3. _____

Expectations and Custom Goal Setting

☐ MY EXPECTATIONS ARE LINING UP WITH MY BELIEF SYSTEM.

LIST 3 "I AM" STATEMENTS:

1. _____
2. _____
3. _____

Reflection – "The Day's Lessons"

EVENT:_____

STUMBLE:_____

TOOL:_____

_____

_____

_____

_____

_____

H.A.P.P.I.N.E.S.S. Victories

LIST 3 EMOTIONAL VICTORIES YOU ACHIEVED TODAY:

1. _____

2. _____

3. _____

NUTRITION

☐ I AM HONORING MY BODY BY HONORING THE GUIDELINES OF MY NUTRITIONAL PLAN.

FITNESS

☐ I AM HONORING MY BODY BY HONORING MY SELECTED FITNESS PLAN.

SUPPORT

☐ I AM RECEIVING SUPPORT

☐ I AM GIVING SUPPORT

LIST 3 PEOPLE YOU RECEIVE SUPPORT FROM OR PROVIDE SUPPORT TO:

1. _____

2. _____

3. _____

MY SUPPORT TEAM IS:

☐ SAFE

☐ EMPATHETIC

☐ SOLUTION-FOCUSED

This is my journey...

MY THOUGHTS DETERMINE WHO I AM,

WHAT I HAVE,

AND WHAT I CAN DO.

THE POWER TO DECIDE MY LIFE RESTS INSIDE OF ME

THROUGH THE HOLY SPIRIT AND I BOLDLY CLAIM

MY RIGHT TO LIVE WITH GRACE AND GLORY ON MY SIDE.

MY THOUGHTS WILL REFLECT A LOVE FOR MYSELF ONLY EQUALED

BY GOD'S LOVE FOR ME.

My mind is alert.

MY HEART IS OPEN AND JOY AND HAPPINESS ARE MY GUIDING LIGHTS.

AMEN.

DAILY BLESSINGS

Day Seventeen: Phase Two

Why do we compare ourselves with others?

We come to know ourselves by comparing ourselves to other people. We compare ourselves to evaluate our opinions and abilities, figure out our strengths and weaknesses, in order to have an accurate view of ourselves.

Comparison in and of itself is not the problem; it is a function of our forebrain and necessary for "self-other mergence."

However, there is a very thin veil between Healthy Comparison and Toxic Comparison.

Upside of Healthy Comparison:
- Gather information
- Reality check to goals
- Boost motivation

Downside of Toxic Comparison:
- Gather information to use against ourselves to further justify or boost our ego
- Reality check to limits
- Demotivation with a sense of hopelessness

Healthy Comparison feels like innocent observation and will always bring you back to self-empowerment. Toxic Comparison feels competitive and evokes a sense of superiority or inferiority.

Until next time, LIVE INSPIRED!

"WITH EVERY RISING OF THE SUN, THINK OF YOUR LIFE AS JUST BEGUN..."

-ROBIN SHEA

GROUND YOUR DAY IN THESE POSITIVE PRACTICES...

DISCOVERY THROUGH JOURNALING

Catalyst Goal - "Shooting Star Goals"

LIST YOUR SHORT-TERM, FEEL-GOOD GOAL FOR THE DAY: _____

_____

_____

Process/Performance Visualization - "Preview of Success"

LIST 3 PROCESS AND/OR PERFORMANCE STRUGGLES:

1. _____

2. _____

3. _____

LIST 3 WAYS YOU ENVISION YOURSELF OVERCOMING THESE 3 OBSTACLES:

1. _____

2. _____

3. _____

Projected Visualization - "Future Self Meditation"

LIST 3 "FUTURE SELF" SCENARIOS IN WHICH YOU ARE LIVING YOUR ENVISIONED LIFE.

1. _____

2. _____

3. _____

Expectations and Custom Goal Setting

☐ MY EXPECTATIONS ARE LINING UP WITH MY BELIEF SYSTEM.

LIST 3 "I AM" STATEMENTS:

1. _____

2. _____

3. _____

END YOUR DAY WITH THESE HELPFUL PRACTICES...

Reflection – "The Day's Lessons"

EVENT:_____

STUMBLE:_____

TOOL:_____

_____

_____

_____

_____

H.A.P.P.I.N.E.S.S. Victories

LIST 3 EMOTIONAL VICTORIES YOU ACHIEVED TODAY:

1. _____

2. _____

3. _____

NUTRITION

☐ I AM HONORING MY BODY BY HONORING THE GUIDELINES OF MY NUTRITIONAL PLAN.

FITNESS

☐ I AM HONORING MY BODY BY HONORING MY SELECTED FITNESS PLAN.

SUPPORT

☐ I AM RECEIVING SUPPORT

☐ I AM GIVING SUPPORT

LIST 3 PEOPLE YOU RECEIVE SUPPORT FROM OR PROVIDE SUPPORT TO:

1. _____

2. _____

3. _____

MY SUPPORT TEAM IS:

☐ SAFE

☐ EMPATHETIC

☐ SOLUTION-FOCUSED

This is my journey...

MY THOUGHTS DETERMINE WHO I AM,

WHAT I HAVE,

AND WHAT I CAN DO.

THE POWER TO DECIDE MY LIFE RESTS INSIDE OF ME

THROUGH THE HOLY SPIRIT AND I BOLDLY CLAIM

MY RIGHT TO LIVE WITH GRACE AND GLORY ON MY SIDE.

MY THOUGHTS WILL REFLECT A LOVE FOR MYSELF ONLY EQUALED

BY GOD'S LOVE FOR ME.

My mind is alert.

MY HEART IS OPEN AND JOY AND HAPPINESS ARE MY GUIDING LIGHTS.

AMEN.

DAILY BLESSINGS

Day Eighteen: Phase Three

Every day holds the gift of experience, perspective, respect for time, appreciation for freedom, story telling, relationships, and reflection. However, we must choose to open our gift, or it becomes our regret.

Trust the magic of new beginnings even if they feel like painful endings. The magic of beginnings is that you take the wisdom of yesterday with you into your new adventure.

There is a space between now and then that you have the power to claim as your "New Beginning." I call this space **Elysian**, a beautiful or creative space that is divinely inspired, peaceful, and perfect.

Many people choose to die "in spirit" today, only to be buried in twenty, thirty, forty years from now. Every day is a new beginning if you just open the gift!

Until next time, LIVE INSPIRED!

GROUND YOUR DAY IN THESE POSITIVE PRACTICES...

DISCOVERY THROUGH JOURNALING

Catalyst Goal - "Shooting Star Goals"

LIST YOUR SHORT-TERM, FEEL-GOOD GOAL FOR THE DAY: _____

_____

_____

Process/Performance Visualization - "Preview of Success"

LIST 3 PROCESS AND/ OR PERFORMANCE STRUGGLES:

1. _____

2. _____

3. _____

LIST 3 WAYS YOU ENVISION YOURSELF OVERCOMING THESE 3 OBSTACLES:

1. _____

2. _____

3. _____

Projected Visualization - "Future Self Meditation"

LIST 3 "FUTURE SELF" SCENARIOS IN WHICH YOU ARE LIVING YOUR ENVISIONED LIFE.

1. _____

2. _____

3. _____

Expectations and Custom Goal Setting

☐ MY EXPECTATIONS ARE LINING UP WITH MY BELIEF SYSTEM.

LIST 3 "I AM" STATEMENTS:

1. _____

2. _____

3. _____

END YOUR DAY WITH THESE HELPFUL PRACTICES...

Reflection – "The Day's Lessons"

EVENT: _____

STUMBLE: _____

TOOL: _____

_____

_____

_____

_____

H.A.P.P.I.N.E.S.S. Victories

LIST 3 EMOTIONAL VICTORIES YOU ACHIEVED TODAY:

1. _____

2. _____

3. _____

NUTRITION

☐ I AM HONORING MY BODY BY HONORING THE GUIDELINES OF MY NUTRITIONAL PLAN.

FITNESS

☐ I AM HONORING MY BODY BY HONORING MY SELECTED FITNESS PLAN.

SUPPORT

☐ I AM RECEIVING SUPPORT

☐ I AM GIVING SUPPORT

LIST 3 PEOPLE YOU RECEIVE SUPPORT FROM OR PROVIDE SUPPORT TO:

1. _____

2. _____

3. _____

MY SUPPORT TEAM IS:

☐ SAFE

☐ EMPATHETIC

☐ SOLUTION-FOCUSED

Robin Shea

This is my journey...

MY THOUGHTS DETERMINE WHO I AM,

WHAT I HAVE,

AND WHAT I CAN DO.

THE POWER TO DECIDE MY LIFE RESTS INSIDE OF ME

THROUGH THE HOLY SPIRIT AND I BOLDLY CLAIM

MY RIGHT TO LIVE WITH GRACE AND GLORY ON MY SIDE.

MY THOUGHTS WILL REFLECT A LOVE FOR MYSELF ONLY EQUALED

BY GOD'S LOVE FOR ME.

My mind is alert.

MY HEART IS OPEN AND JOY AND HAPPINESS ARE MY GUIDING LIGHTS.

AMEN.

DAILY BLESSINGS

Day Nineteen: Phase Three

If we sharpen our senses, we can feel our way through life using the subtle guidance of our internal navigational system. It is the ability to rest into, and respect, the Universe's desire. to guide our life to our Desired Self.

When you create a STRONG vision of your Desired Self, your internal navigational system will lock-in and gently guide you to the vision you present.

Pain is a great indicator that you have turned away from your path. Some people spend a lifetime struggling with this reality. They continue experiencing the same pain, in the same circumstances, over and over again. They never make the connection between pain and path.

But those of us that respect and embrace pain as our greatest teacher look forward to identifying the cause and learning to move away from it to get back on our path.

Pain is a necessary part of our journey. But, experiencing pain for pain's sake is a wasted opportunity to identify a more joyous path.

Until next time, LIVE INSPIRED!

"WITH EVERY RISING OF THE SUN, THINK OF YOUR LIFE AS JUST BEGUN . . ."

-ROBIN SHEA

GROUND YOUR DAY IN THESE POSITIVE PRACTICES . . .

DISCOVERY THROUGH JOURNALING

Catalyst Goal - "Shooting Star Goals"

LIST YOUR SHORT-TERM, FEEL-GOOD GOAL FOR THE DAY: _____

_____

_____

Process/Performance Visualization - "Preview of Success"

LIST 3 PROCESS AND/OR PERFORMANCE STRUGGLES:

1. _____

2. _____

3. _____

LIST 3 WAYS YOU ENVISION YOURSELF OVERCOMING THESE 3 OBSTACLES:

1. _____

2. _____

3. _____

Projected Visualization - "Future Self Meditation"

LIST 3 "FUTURE SELF" SCENARIOS IN WHICH YOU ARE LIVING YOUR ENVISIONED LIFE.

1. _____

2. _____

3. _____

Expectations and Custom Goal Setting

☐ MY EXPECTATIONS ARE LINING UP WITH MY BELIEF SYSTEM.

LIST 3 "I AM" STATEMENTS:

1. _____

2. _____

3. _____

Reflection – "The Day's Lessons"

EVENT:———————————————————————————————————

STUMBLE:—————————————————————————————————

TOOL:————————————————————————————————————

———————————————————————————————————————

———————————————————————————————————————

———————————————————————————————————————

———————————————————————————————————————

H.A.P.P.I.N.E.S.S. Victories

LIST 3 EMOTIONAL VICTORIES YOU ACHIEVED TODAY:

1. ————————————————————————————————————

2. ————————————————————————————————————

3. ————————————————————————————————————

NUTRITION

☐ I AM HONORING MY BODY BY HONORING THE GUIDELINES OF MY NUTRITIONAL PLAN.

FITNESS

☐ I AM HONORING MY BODY BY HONORING MY SELECTED FITNESS PLAN.

SUPPORT

☐ I AM RECEIVING SUPPORT

☐ I AM GIVING SUPPORT

LIST 3 PEOPLE YOU RECEIVE SUPPORT FROM OR PROVIDE SUPPORT TO:

1. ————————————————————————————————————

2. ————————————————————————————————————

3. ————————————————————————————————————

MY SUPPORT TEAM IS:

☐ SAFE

☐ EMPATHETIC

☐ SOLUTION-FOCUSED

This is my journey...

MY THOUGHTS DETERMINE WHO I AM,

WHAT I HAVE,

AND WHAT I CAN DO.

THE POWER TO DECIDE MY LIFE RESTS INSIDE OF ME

THROUGH THE HOLY SPIRIT AND I BOLDLY CLAIM

MY RIGHT TO LIVE WITH GRACE AND GLORY ON MY SIDE.

MY THOUGHTS WILL REFLECT A LOVE FOR MYSELF ONLY EQUALED

BY GOD'S LOVE FOR ME.

My mind is alert.

MY HEART IS OPEN AND JOY AND HAPPINESS ARE MY GUIDING LIGHTS.

AMEN.

DAILY BLESSINGS

Day Twenty: Phase Three

Some people use excuses to avoid a task, and others use an excuse to clear the path for a task.

Marcus Luttrell, the "Lone Survivor," tells his heroic story of survival in which he, as the only survivor of a team of five Navy Seals, managed to crawl seven miles to evade capture.

With a shattered body and paralyzed from the waist down, Luttrell used a rock and stretched his arm out as far away from his body as possible and drew a line in the earth. He would then crawl to the line and repeat the process eventually dragging his broken body seven-miles to safety.

Marcus had every reason to quit. His circumstance was an excuse to fail should he have chosen to look in that direction, but rather than finding excuses to quit, he found excuses to live; and with a simple rock, he inched his way out of danger. Every single moment mattered. Every breath directed to life mattered. Every small victory mattered. Life mattered. He didn't think beyond the rock, but the rock saved his life.

When you find yourself struggling with the big picture, focus on one single act and do it with precision.

Until next time, LIVE INSPIRED!

"WITH EVERY RISING OF THE SUN, THINK OF YOUR LIFE AS JUST BEGUN..."

-ROBIN SHEA

GROUND YOUR DAY IN THESE POSITIVE PRACTICES...

DISCOVERY THROUGH JOURNALING

Catalyst Goal - "Shooting Star Goals"

LIST YOUR SHORT-TERM, FEEL-GOOD GOAL FOR THE DAY: _____

_____

_____

Process/Performance Visualization - "Preview of Success"

LIST 3 PROCESS AND/OR PERFORMANCE STRUGGLES:

1. _____
2. _____
3. _____

LIST 3 WAYS YOU ENVISION YOURSELF OVERCOMING THESE 3 OBSTACLES:

1. _____
2. _____
3. _____

Projected Visualization - "Future Self Meditation"

LIST 3 "FUTURE SELF" SCENARIOS IN WHICH YOU ARE LIVING YOUR ENVISIONED LIFE.

1. _____
2. _____
3. _____

Expectations and Custom Goal Setting

☐   MY EXPECTATIONS ARE LINING UP WITH MY BELIEF SYSTEM.

LIST 3 "I AM" STATEMENTS:

1. _____
2. _____
3. _____

Reflection – "The Day's Lessons"

EVENT:—————————————————————————————

STUMBLE:————————————————————————————

TOOL:——————————————————————————————

———————————————————————————————————

———————————————————————————————————

———————————————————————————————————

———————————————————————————————————

H.A.P.P.I.N.E.S.S. Victories

LIST 3 EMOTIONAL VICTORIES YOU ACHIEVED TODAY:

1. ———————————————————————————————

2. ———————————————————————————————

3. ———————————————————————————————

NUTRITION

☐ I AM HONORING MY BODY BY HONORING THE GUIDELINES OF MY NUTRITIONAL PLAN.

FITNESS

☐ I AM HONORING MY BODY BY HONORING MY SELECTED FITNESS PLAN.

SUPPORT

☐ I AM RECEIVING SUPPORT

☐ I AM GIVING SUPPORT

LIST 3 PEOPLE YOU RECEIVE SUPPORT FROM OR PROVIDE SUPPORT TO:

1. ———————————————————————————————

2. ———————————————————————————————

3. ———————————————————————————————

MY SUPPORT TEAM IS:

☐ SAFE

☐ EMPATHETIC

☐ SOLUTION-FOCUSED

This is my journey...

MY THOUGHTS DETERMINE WHO I AM,

WHAT I HAVE,

AND WHAT I CAN DO.

THE POWER TO DECIDE MY LIFE RESTS INSIDE OF ME

THROUGH THE HOLY SPIRIT AND I BOLDLY CLAIM

MY RIGHT TO LIVE WITH GRACE AND GLORY ON MY SIDE.

MY THOUGHTS WILL REFLECT A LOVE FOR MYSELF ONLY EQUALED

BY GOD'S LOVE FOR ME.

My mind is alert.

MY HEART IS OPEN AND JOY AND HAPPINESS ARE MY GUIDING LIGHTS.

AMEN.

DAILY BLESSINGS

Day Twenty-One: Phase Three

If you worked the three previous phases of the program as prescribed, you should be TIRED! Engaging your conscious mind is as exhausting (often more exhausting) than running a marathon. You have spent the past 21 days actively engaging 5% of your mind, asking it to take the wheel and reinvent your life.

The ultimate goal is to reinvent your default behaviors with the new behaviors created by engaging your Conscious Mind (the 5%). Once the new behaviors transfer from the conscious to the subconscious, you have created a new AUTOMATIC Pilot!

Let's look at what you have asked of your conscious mind over the past 21 days!

Typically, out of a 12-hour period, we only engage our conscious mind 40 minutes; the remaining 11 hours and 20 minutes are spent on autopilot.

You have trained your mind like an athlete trains their body, asking your mind to go above and beyond, stretching and flexing, forcing your thinking outside of its box and asking it to elevate its standards, problem solve, celebrate and FOCUS, FOCUS, FOCUS.

It's GAME TIME... Our goal for the final phase of the program is to see what has stuck from the training. Assess its efficacy and prepare to begin again with a new set point.

Until next time, LIVE INSPIRED!

"WITH EVERY RISING OF THE SUN, THINK OF YOUR LIFE AS JUST BEGUN..."

-ROBIN SHEA

GROUND YOUR DAY IN THESE POSITIVE PRACTICES...

DISCOVERY THROUGH JOURNALING

Catalyst Goal - "Shooting Star Goals"

LIST YOUR SHORT-TERM, FEEL-GOOD GOAL FOR THE DAY: _____

_____

_____

Process/Performance Visualization - "Preview of Success"

LIST 3 PROCESS AND/OR PERFORMANCE STRUGGLES:

1. _____
2. _____
3. _____

LIST 3 WAYS YOU ENVISION YOURSELF OVERCOMING THESE 3 OBSTACLES:

1. _____
2. _____
3. _____

Projected Visualization - "Future Self Meditation"

LIST 3 "FUTURE SELF" SCENARIOS IN WHICH YOU ARE LIVING YOUR ENVISIONED LIFE.

1. _____
2. _____
3. _____

Expectations and Custom Goal Setting

☐ MY EXPECTATIONS ARE LINING UP WITH MY BELIEF SYSTEM.

LIST 3 "I AM" STATEMENTS:

1. _____
2. _____
3. _____

Reflection – "The Day's Lessons"

EVENT:————————————————————————————————————

STUMBLE:————————————————————————————————

TOOL:————————————————————————————————————

——

——

——

——

H.A.P.P.I.N.E.S.S. Victories

LIST 3 EMOTIONAL VICTORIES YOU ACHIEVED TODAY:

1. ———————————————————————————————————

2. ———————————————————————————————————

3. ———————————————————————————————————

NUTRITION

☐ I AM HONORING MY BODY BY HONORING THE GUIDELINES OF MY NUTRITIONAL PLAN.

FITNESS

☐ I AM HONORING MY BODY BY HONORING MY SELECTED FITNESS PLAN.

SUPPORT

☐ I AM RECEIVING SUPPORT

☐ I AM GIVING SUPPORT

LIST 3 PEOPLE YOU RECEIVE SUPPORT FROM OR PROVIDE SUPPORT TO:

1. ———————————————————————————————————

2. ———————————————————————————————————

3. ———————————————————————————————————

MY SUPPORT TEAM IS:

☐ SAFE

☐ EMPATHETIC

☐ SOLUTION-FOCUSED

This is my journey...

MY THOUGHTS DETERMINE WHO I AM,

WHAT I HAVE,

AND WHAT I CAN DO.

THE POWER TO DECIDE MY LIFE RESTS INSIDE OF ME

THROUGH THE HOLY SPIRIT AND I BOLDLY CLAIM

MY RIGHT TO LIVE WITH GRACE AND GLORY ON MY SIDE.

MY THOUGHTS WILL REFLECT A LOVE FOR MYSELF ONLY EQUALED

BY GOD'S LOVE FOR ME.

My mind is alert.

MY HEART IS OPEN AND JOY AND HAPPINESS ARE MY GUIDING LIGHTS.

AMEN.

DAILY BLESSINGS

Day Twenty-Two: Phase Three

The price you pay for change is relative to the clarity of your vision. The clearer, more compelling vision you create, the less distracted you are by the cost.

Your willingness to act is directly related to the emotional energy attached to the transformation. For example, losing weight for a high school reunion is easier than losing weight to have a longer, healthier life. You can see how using **Catalyst Goals** (short-term goals) to support **Projected Imagery** (long-term goals) is very effective.

A Catalyst Goal (short-term goal) will have more emotional energy, which will amp up your willpower and help you turn away from temptation while reinventing your behavior. This supports your ultimate goal of living a longer, healthier life.

When the price feels too high, it only means your vision does not have enough emotional energy; so use Catalyst Goals to breathe more intensity into your transformation.

Projected Imagery (long-term goals) supported by intermittent Catalyst Goals (short-term goals) is a great strategy. Just remember, Catalyst Goals alone are rarely enough to transform your life permanently. They're like shooting stars: they burn the brightest but burn out the fastest.

Until next time, LIVE INSPIRED!

"WITH EVERY RISING OF THE SUN, THINK OF YOUR LIFE AS JUST BEGUN..."

-ROBIN SHEA

GROUND YOUR DAY IN THESE POSITIVE PRACTICES...

DISCOVERY THROUGH JOURNALING

Catalyst Goal - "Shooting Star Goals"

LIST YOUR SHORT-TERM, FEEL-GOOD GOAL FOR THE DAY: _____

_____

_____

Process/Performance Visualization - "Preview of Success"

LIST 3 PROCESS AND/OR PERFORMANCE STRUGGLES:

1. _____
2. _____
3. _____

LIST 3 WAYS YOU ENVISION YOURSELF OVERCOMING THESE 3 OBSTACLES:

1. _____
2. _____
3. _____

Projected Visualization - "Future Self Meditation"

LIST 3 "FUTURE SELF" SCENARIOS IN WHICH YOU ARE LIVING YOUR ENVISIONED LIFE.

1. _____
2. _____
3. _____

Expectations and Custom Goal Setting

☐   MY EXPECTATIONS ARE LINING UP WITH MY BELIEF SYSTEM.

LIST 3 "I AM" STATEMENTS:

1. _____
2. _____
3. _____

Reflection – "The Day's Lessons"

EVENT:

STUMBLE:

TOOL:

H.A.P.P.I.N.E.S.S. Victories

LIST 3 EMOTIONAL VICTORIES YOU ACHIEVED TODAY:

1.

2.

3.

NUTRITION

☐ I AM HONORING MY BODY BY HONORING THE GUIDELINES OF MY NUTRITIONAL PLAN.

FITNESS

☐ I AM HONORING MY BODY BY HONORING MY SELECTED FITNESS PLAN.

SUPPORT

☐ I AM RECEIVING SUPPORT

☐ I AM GIVING SUPPORT

LIST 3 PEOPLE YOU RECEIVE SUPPORT FROM OR PROVIDE SUPPORT TO:

1.

2.

3.

MY SUPPORT TEAM IS:

☐ SAFE

☐ EMPATHETIC

☐ SOLUTION-FOCUSED

This is my journey...

MY THOUGHTS DETERMINE WHO I AM,

WHAT I HAVE,

AND WHAT I CAN DO.

THE POWER TO DECIDE MY LIFE RESTS INSIDE OF ME

THROUGH THE HOLY SPIRIT AND I BOLDLY CLAIM

MY RIGHT TO LIVE WITH GRACE AND GLORY ON MY SIDE.

MY THOUGHTS WILL REFLECT A LOVE FOR MYSELF ONLY EQUALED

BY GOD'S LOVE FOR ME.

My mind is alert.

MY HEART IS OPEN AND JOY AND HAPPINESS ARE MY GUIDING LIGHTS.

AMEN.

DAILY BLESSINGS

Day Twenty-Three: Phase Three

Sharpening your tools is part of the process. For healthy transformation, this means being prepared. Always have healthy snacks readily available, never allow yourself to get too hungry, get enough rest (rest restores your coping hormones), eat every 2-3 hours, know your binge triggers, minimize (or eliminate) alcohol, and journal every day!

Your toolbox will contain tools unique to you, but building this toolbox is not optional; it is imperative to your success.

Take time to write down a plan of action when facing challenging circumstances and watch your plan come to life.

Replace desperation with preparation.

Until next time, LIVE INSPIRED!

"WITH EVERY RISING OF THE SUN, THINK OF YOUR LIFE AS JUST BEGUN..."

-ROBIN SHEA

GROUND YOUR DAY IN THESE POSITIVE PRACTICES...

DISCOVERY THROUGH JOURNALING

Catalyst Goal - "Shooting Star Goals"

LIST YOUR SHORT-TERM, FEEL-GOOD GOAL FOR THE DAY: _____

_____

_____

Process/Performance Visualization - "Preview of Success"

LIST 3 PROCESS AND/ OR PERFORMANCE STRUGGLES:

1. _____
2. _____
3. _____

LIST 3 WAYS YOU ENVISION YOURSELF OVERCOMING THESE 3 OBSTACLES:

1. _____
2. _____
3. _____

Projected Visualization - "Future Self Meditation"

LIST 3 "FUTURE SELF" SCENARIOS IN WHICH YOU ARE LIVING YOUR ENVISIONED LIFE.

1. _____
2. _____
3. _____

Expectations and Custom Goal Setting

☐ MY EXPECTATIONS ARE LINING UP WITH MY BELIEF SYSTEM.

LIST 3 "I AM" STATEMENTS:

1. _____
2. _____
3. _____

END YOUR DAY WITH THESE HELPFUL PRACTICES . . .

Reflection – "The Day's Lessons"

EVENT:

STUMBLE:

TOOL:

H.A.P.P.I.N.E.S.S. Victories

LIST 3 EMOTIONAL VICTORIES YOU ACHIEVED TODAY:

1.

2.

3.

NUTRITION

☐ I AM HONORING MY BODY BY HONORING THE GUIDELINES OF MY NUTRITIONAL PLAN.

FITNESS

☐ I AM HONORING MY BODY BY HONORING MY SELECTED FITNESS PLAN.

SUPPORT

☐ I AM RECEIVING SUPPORT

☐ I AM GIVING SUPPORT

LIST 3 PEOPLE YOU RECEIVE SUPPORT FROM OR PROVIDE SUPPORT TO:

1.

2.

3.

MY SUPPORT TEAM IS:

☐ SAFE

☐ EMPATHETIC

☐ SOLUTION-FOCUSED

Robin Shea

This is my journey...

MY THOUGHTS DETERMINE WHO I AM,

WHAT I HAVE,

AND WHAT I CAN DO.

THE POWER TO DECIDE MY LIFE RESTS INSIDE OF ME

THROUGH THE HOLY SPIRIT AND I BOLDLY CLAIM

MY RIGHT TO LIVE WITH GRACE AND GLORY ON MY SIDE.

MY THOUGHTS WILL REFLECT A LOVE FOR MYSELF ONLY EQUALED

BY GOD'S LOVE FOR ME.

My mind is alert.

MY HEART IS OPEN AND JOY AND HAPPINESS ARE MY GUIDING LIGHTS.

AMEN.

DAILY BLESSINGS

Day Twenty-Four: Phase Three

One of the most valuable qualities you can develop is **Instinct**. But how do you tell the difference between an Instinct and its evil twin, **Impulse**?

On the surface, Impulse looks a lot like an Instinct: it comes from inside, and it's a powerful force urging you to do something. The greatest distinction between the two is this: Instinct pulls us toward our Desired Self, and Impulse pushes us away from our Desired Self.

Impulses are DESTRUCTIVE and DISTRACTING, they and try to keep you tied to familiar. They tempt us with damaging, self-soothing habits and nonproductive, time-wasting distractions. Impulses seem to help reduce stress, but guess what? They only provide a momentary relief followed by higher levels of stress, coupled with guilt and frustration.

Instincts, on the other-hand, often challenge us to move out of the familiar. Because our instincts challenge the status quo, we often get in the habit of ignoring their signal. It becomes harder to recognize them. Or, worse, they go underground and turn into depression if you ignore them long enough. Instincts are SUPPORTIVE, FOCUSED, and ACTIONABLE; they keep us moving toward our desires. They challenge us with problem-solving skills, trust, and often nonsensical, actions. Our instincts maintain an uninterrupted connection to our source.

Learning to discern between impulse and instinct is a valuable tool of self-actualization.

Until next time, LIVE INSPIRED!

"WITH EVERY RISING OF THE SUN, THINK OF YOUR LIFE AS JUST BEGUN..."

-ROBIN SHEA

GROUND YOUR DAY IN THESE POSITIVE PRACTICES...

DISCOVERY THROUGH JOURNALING

Catalyst Goal - "Shooting Star Goals"

LIST YOUR SHORT-TERM, FEEL-GOOD GOAL FOR THE DAY: _____

_____

_____

Process/Performance Visualization - "Preview of Success"

LIST 3 PROCESS AND/OR PERFORMANCE STRUGGLES:

1. _____

2. _____

3. _____

LIST 3 WAYS YOU ENVISION YOURSELF OVERCOMING THESE 3 OBSTACLES:

1. _____

2. _____

3. _____

Projected Visualization - "Future Self Meditation"

LIST 3 "FUTURE SELF" SCENARIOS IN WHICH YOU ARE LIVING YOUR ENVISIONED LIFE.

1. _____

2. _____

3. _____

Expectations and Custom Goal Setting

☐ MY EXPECTATIONS ARE LINING UP WITH MY BELIEF SYSTEM.

LIST 3 "I AM" STATEMENTS:

1. _____

2. _____

3. _____

Reflection – "The Day's Lessons"

EVENT:⎯⎯⎯⎯⎯⎯⎯⎯⎯⎯⎯⎯⎯⎯⎯⎯⎯⎯⎯⎯⎯⎯⎯

STUMBLE:⎯⎯⎯⎯⎯⎯⎯⎯⎯⎯⎯⎯⎯⎯⎯⎯⎯⎯⎯⎯⎯

TOOL:⎯⎯⎯⎯⎯⎯⎯⎯⎯⎯⎯⎯⎯⎯⎯⎯⎯⎯⎯⎯⎯⎯⎯

H.A.P.P.I.N.E.S.S. Victories

LIST 3 EMOTIONAL VICTORIES YOU ACHIEVED TODAY:

1. ⎯⎯⎯⎯⎯⎯⎯⎯⎯⎯⎯⎯⎯⎯⎯⎯⎯⎯⎯⎯⎯⎯⎯⎯
2. ⎯⎯⎯⎯⎯⎯⎯⎯⎯⎯⎯⎯⎯⎯⎯⎯⎯⎯⎯⎯⎯⎯⎯⎯
3. ⎯⎯⎯⎯⎯⎯⎯⎯⎯⎯⎯⎯⎯⎯⎯⎯⎯⎯⎯⎯⎯⎯⎯⎯

NUTRITION

☐ I AM HONORING MY BODY BY HONORING THE GUIDELINES OF MY NUTRITIONAL PLAN.

FITNESS

☐ I AM HONORING MY BODY BY HONORING MY SELECTED FITNESS PLAN.

SUPPORT

☐ I AM RECEIVING SUPPORT

☐ I AM GIVING SUPPORT

LIST 3 PEOPLE YOU RECEIVE SUPPORT FROM OR PROVIDE SUPPORT TO:

1. ⎯⎯⎯⎯⎯⎯⎯⎯⎯⎯⎯⎯⎯⎯⎯⎯⎯⎯⎯⎯⎯⎯⎯⎯
2. ⎯⎯⎯⎯⎯⎯⎯⎯⎯⎯⎯⎯⎯⎯⎯⎯⎯⎯⎯⎯⎯⎯⎯⎯
3. ⎯⎯⎯⎯⎯⎯⎯⎯⎯⎯⎯⎯⎯⎯⎯⎯⎯⎯⎯⎯⎯⎯⎯⎯

MY SUPPORT TEAM IS:

☐ SAFE

☐ EMPATHETIC

☐ SOLUTION-FOCUSED

This is my journey...

MY THOUGHTS DETERMINE WHO I AM,

WHAT I HAVE,

AND WHAT I CAN DO.

THE POWER TO DECIDE MY LIFE RESTS INSIDE OF ME

THROUGH THE HOLY SPIRIT AND I BOLDLY CLAIM

MY RIGHT TO LIVE WITH GRACE AND GLORY ON MY SIDE.

MY THOUGHTS WILL REFLECT A LOVE FOR MYSELF ONLY EQUALED

BY GOD'S LOVE FOR ME.

My mind is alert.

MY HEART IS OPEN AND JOY AND HAPPINESS ARE MY GUIDING LIGHTS.

AMEN.

DAILY BLESSINGS

Day Twenty-Five: Phase Four

Transformation while maintaining a state of Joy and Inspiration is a system and not a goal. Let's take a closer look:

The Desired Self
(RECIPE)

The Six Pillars of Support
(INGREDIENTS)

The Four Phases of Transformation
(COOKING STEPS)

Every morning bakers and chefs begin their day with a recipe in hand. Once the recipe is decided upon (Desired Self), they gather their ingredients (Six Pillars), assemble their tools, and begin preparing their dish (Four Phases).

Some recipes are so committed to memory that the process seems effortless; while others require focused attention. Either way, a recipe is followed, and a result is created.

Your Recipe for Success is no different. Every day is a new chance to prepare your recipe (Desired Self). It's an opportunity for you to master the basics, experiment, get creative and grow as the Master Chef of your life.

Until next time, LIVE INSPIRED!

"WITH EVERY RISING OF THE SUN, THINK OF YOUR LIFE AS JUST BEGUN . . ."

-ROBIN SHEA

GROUND YOUR DAY IN THESE POSITIVE PRACTICES . . .

DISCOVERY THROUGH JOURNALING

Catalyst Goal - "Shooting Star Goals"

LIST YOUR SHORT-TERM, FEEL-GOOD GOAL FOR THE DAY: _____

_____

_____

Process/Performance Visualization - "Preview of Success"

LIST 3 PROCESS AND/OR PERFORMANCE STRUGGLES:

1. _____
2. _____
3. _____

LIST 3 WAYS YOU ENVISION YOURSELF OVERCOMING THESE 3 OBSTACLES:

1. _____
2. _____
3. _____

Projected Visualization - "Future Self Meditation"

LIST 3 "FUTURE SELF" SCENARIOS IN WHICH YOU ARE LIVING YOUR ENVISIONED LIFE.

1. _____
2. _____
3. _____

Expectations and Custom Goal Setting

☐ MY EXPECTATIONS ARE LINING UP WITH MY BELIEF SYSTEM.

LIST 3 "I AM" STATEMENTS:

1. _____
2. _____
3. _____

END YOUR DAY WITH THESE HELPFUL PRACTICES...

Reflection – "The Day's Lessons"

EVENT:

STUMBLE:

TOOL:

H.A.P.P.I.N.E.S.S. Victories

LIST 3 EMOTIONAL VICTORIES YOU ACHIEVED TODAY:

1.

2.

3.

NUTRITION

☐ I AM HONORING MY BODY BY HONORING THE GUIDELINES OF MY NUTRITIONAL PLAN.

FITNESS

☐ I AM HONORING MY BODY BY HONORING MY SELECTED FITNESS PLAN.

SUPPORT

☐ I AM RECEIVING SUPPORT

☐ I AM GIVING SUPPORT

LIST 3 PEOPLE YOU RECEIVE SUPPORT FROM OR PROVIDE SUPPORT TO:

1.

2.

3.

MY SUPPORT TEAM IS:

☐ SAFE

☐ EMPATHETIC

☐ SOLUTION-FOCUSED

This is my journey...

MY THOUGHTS DETERMINE WHO I AM,

WHAT I HAVE,

AND WHAT I CAN DO.

THE POWER TO DECIDE MY LIFE RESTS INSIDE OF ME

THROUGH THE HOLY SPIRIT AND I BOLDLY CLAIM

MY RIGHT TO LIVE WITH GRACE AND GLORY ON MY SIDE.

MY THOUGHTS WILL REFLECT A LOVE FOR MYSELF ONLY EQUALED

BY GOD'S LOVE FOR ME.

My mind is alert.

MY HEART IS OPEN AND JOY AND HAPPINESS ARE MY GUIDING LIGHTS.

AMEN.

DAILY BLESSINGS

Day Twenty-Six: Phase Four

I have invested thirteen plus years creating a system for healthy lifestyle transformation through a state of Joy and Inspiration that ANYONE can follow!

All I have ever wanted to do was SHARE this gift with others. Sharing nourished my soul, reinforced my new habits and gave my life purpose beyond raising my children.

In two short days you will reach the end of your first transformation cycle. How does your heart feel about sharing now?

Is there anyone in your life who has watched your journey and could benefit from a transformation? If they are open to the idea, maybe it would be wonderful to ask them to join you in your next transformation cycle.

If not, no worries! I have been working this system for over thirteen years; sometimes along the way I have had someone in my life that wanted to go through a cycle with me, but much of that time was spent learning about myself and traveling alone. Either way, this is your journey, so embrace it!

Until next time, LIVE INSPIRED!

GROUND YOUR DAY IN THESE POSITIVE PRACTICES...

DISCOVERY THROUGH JOURNALING

Catalyst Goal - "Shooting Star Goals"

LIST YOUR SHORT-TERM, FEEL-GOOD GOAL FOR THE DAY: _____

_____

_____

Process/Performance Visualization - "Preview of Success"

LIST 3 PROCESS AND/OR PERFORMANCE STRUGGLES:

1. _____
2. _____
3. _____

LIST 3 WAYS YOU ENVISION YOURSELF OVERCOMING THESE 3 OBSTACLES:

1. _____
2. _____
3. _____

Projected Visualization - "Future Self Meditation"

LIST 3 "FUTURE SELF" SCENARIOS IN WHICH YOU ARE LIVING YOUR ENVISIONED LIFE.

1. _____
2. _____
3. _____

Expectations and Custom Goal Setting

☐ MY EXPECTATIONS ARE LINING UP WITH MY BELIEF SYSTEM.

LIST 3 "I AM" STATEMENTS:

1. _____
2. _____
3. _____

END YOUR DAY WITH THESE HELPFUL PRACTICES...

Reflection – "The Day's Lessons"

EVENT:———————————————————————————

STUMBLE:—————————————————————————

TOOL:——————————————————————————

———————————————————————————————

———————————————————————————————

———————————————————————————————

———————————————————————————————

———————————————————————————————

H.A.P.P.I.N.E.S.S. Victories

LIST 3 EMOTIONAL VICTORIES YOU ACHIEVED TODAY:

1. ——————————————————————————————

2. ——————————————————————————————

3. ——————————————————————————————

NUTRITION

☐ I AM HONORING MY BODY BY HONORING THE GUIDELINES OF MY NUTRITIONAL PLAN.

FITNESS

☐ I AM HONORING MY BODY BY HONORING MY SELECTED FITNESS PLAN.

SUPPORT

☐ I AM RECEIVING SUPPORT

☐ I AM GIVING SUPPORT

LIST 3 PEOPLE YOU RECEIVE SUPPORT FROM OR PROVIDE SUPPORT TO:

1. ——————————————————————————————

2. ——————————————————————————————

3. ——————————————————————————————

MY SUPPORT TEAM IS:

☐ SAFE

☐ EMPATHETIC

☐ SOLUTION-FOCUSED

This is my journey...

MY THOUGHTS DETERMINE WHO I AM,

WHAT I HAVE,

AND WHAT I CAN DO.

THE POWER TO DECIDE MY LIFE RESTS INSIDE OF ME

THROUGH THE HOLY SPIRIT AND I BOLDLY CLAIM

MY RIGHT TO LIVE WITH GRACE AND GLORY ON MY SIDE.

MY THOUGHTS WILL REFLECT A LOVE FOR MYSELF ONLY EQUALED

BY GOD'S LOVE FOR ME.

My mind is alert.

MY HEART IS OPEN AND JOY AND HAPPINESS ARE MY GUIDING LIGHTS.

AMEN.

DAILY BLESSINGS

Day Twenty-Seven: Phase Four

Can it be that simple? Is it possible that Utopia is only an emotion away? Are we that powerful? Is learning to turn away from anger, hate, self-loathing, judgment, guilt and shame and toward love, kindness, self-acceptance, joy, and happiness the KEY to UNLOCKING our HIGHEST POTENTIAL?

You better believe it is... I successfully reclaimed my family's dinner table, nutrition and joy in 2002 with one simple ingredient: the H.A.P.P.I.N.E.S.S. Ladder. The rest was revealed to me slowly, steadily, and precisely. I played a seek-and-find game for over 13 years, patiently allowing each step to be revealed to me when I (the student) was ready.

Every time I wanted to walk away, I was brought back to my "Why Story" and reminded of the power of intention. My transformation inspired me to share my message with others, and I committed my life to discovering the connection between changing habits, nutrition and exercise, self-awareness and the role joy and happiness play in lasting change.

This was my journey. I needed thirteen years of resolve; I needed every struggle, every victory, every peaceful rest, every dead-end search, and every brilliant discovery. I carved my own path, and my journey allows me to sit here in front of you today with 110% confidence in the program I have created as being a Universal, GAME CHANGING approach to healthy lifestyle transformation.

My heart beats for the creation of H.A.P.P.I.N.E.S.S. and a more joyous life, a life that fills me from the inside out!

Until next time, LIVE INSPIRED!

"WITH EVERY RISING OF THE SUN, THINK OF YOUR LIFE AS JUST BEGUN..."

-ROBIN SHEA

GROUND YOUR DAY IN THESE POSITIVE PRACTICES...

DISCOVERY THROUGH JOURNALING

Catalyst Goal - "Shooting Star Goals"

LIST YOUR SHORT-TERM, FEEL-GOOD GOAL FOR THE DAY: _____

_____

_____

Process/Performance Visualization - "Preview of Success"

LIST 3 PROCESS AND/OR PERFORMANCE STRUGGLES:

1. _____

2. _____

3. _____

LIST 3 WAYS YOU ENVISION YOURSELF OVERCOMING THESE 3 OBSTACLES:

1. _____

2. _____

3. _____

Projected Visualization - "Future Self Meditation"

LIST 3 "FUTURE SELF" SCENARIOS IN WHICH YOU ARE LIVING YOUR ENVISIONED LIFE.

1. _____

2. _____

3. _____

Expectations and Custom Goal Setting

☐ MY EXPECTATIONS ARE LINING UP WITH MY BELIEF SYSTEM.

LIST 3 "I AM" STATEMENTS:

1. _____

2. _____

3. _____

END YOUR DAY WITH THESE HELPFUL PRACTICES...

Reflection – "The Day's Lessons"

EVENT:

STUMBLE:

TOOL:

H.A.P.P.I.N.E.S.S. Victories

LIST 3 EMOTIONAL VICTORIES YOU ACHIEVED TODAY:

1.
2.
3.

NUTRITION

☐ I AM HONORING MY BODY BY HONORING THE GUIDELINES OF MY NUTRITIONAL PLAN.

FITNESS

☐ I AM HONORING MY BODY BY HONORING MY SELECTED FITNESS PLAN.

SUPPORT

☐ I AM RECEIVING SUPPORT

☐ I AM GIVING SUPPORT

LIST 3 PEOPLE YOU RECEIVE SUPPORT FROM OR PROVIDE SUPPORT TO:

1.
2.
3.

MY SUPPORT TEAM IS:

☐ SAFE

☐ EMPATHETIC

☐ SOLUTION-FOCUSED

This is my journey...

MY THOUGHTS DETERMINE WHO I AM,

WHAT I HAVE,

AND WHAT I CAN DO.

THE POWER TO DECIDE MY LIFE RESTS INSIDE OF ME

THROUGH THE HOLY SPIRIT AND I BOLDLY CLAIM

MY RIGHT TO LIVE WITH GRACE AND GLORY ON MY SIDE.

MY THOUGHTS WILL REFLECT A LOVE FOR MYSELF ONLY EQUALED

BY GOD'S LOVE FOR ME.

My mind is alert.

MY HEART IS OPEN AND JOY AND HAPPINESS ARE MY GUIDING LIGHTS.

AMEN.

DAILY BLESSINGS

Day Twenty-Eight: Phase Four

Congratulations! If you are reading this, you have reached the final day of the Four Phases of Transformation, and that alone means you are part of the ELITE 2%.

You remember the statistic, right? Ninety-eight percent of people who attempt a diet FAILS and only two percent succeed in actually changing their life! You are now part of that two percent, and that is an amazing accomplishment.

I can tell you something with certainty: you got out of the Four Phases of Transformation exactly what you put into them. Success is nothing more than a few simple disciplines, practiced every day. You can choose to eat a candy bar every day for a snack or an apple, but I can promise you this: if you choose the apple, the result will be very different.

If you worked my system respecting the disciplines I teach, and you lived within those teachings, you achieved one result. If you cheated the disciplines and used them as loosely interpreted guidelines, you got a very different result.

When I said you that you must strictly follow your chosen nutritional program and fitness program, I meant it! When I said that you must completely ENJOY your break time, I meant that, too. To be successful, your focus has to be so intense that others think you have lost your mind.

I know when I transformed my life everyone thought I was crazy! Seriously, they laughed, questioned, shook their heads, prayed for me, sent me messages of comfort; they talked in code around me, they labeled me "nuts." Then, they became quieter, they began asking questions, and they watched timidly. The wheels began turning in their heads. Finally, they approached me humbly, they asked for guidance, and they thanked me!

Before the days turn into weeks, and the weeks turn into months, REPEAT the Four Phases of Transformation and invite a friend to join you! Mentor them, share your knowledge because by sharing your heart, you will be more deeply strengthening your neural connections. This is a pay-it-forward program.

Your success is my greatest honor!

Until next time... LIVE INSPIRED!

"WITH EVERY RISING OF THE SUN, THINK OF YOUR LIFE AS JUST BEGUN . . ."

-ROBIN SHEA

GROUND YOUR DAY IN THESE POSITIVE PRACTICES . . .

DISCOVERY THROUGH JOURNALING

Catalyst Goal - "Shooting Star Goals"

LIST YOUR SHORT-TERM, FEEL-GOOD GOAL FOR THE DAY: _____

_____

_____

Process/Performance Visualization - "Preview of Success"

LIST 3 PROCESS AND/ OR PERFORMANCE STRUGGLES:

1. _____
2. _____
3. _____

LIST 3 WAYS YOU ENVISION YOURSELF OVERCOMING THESE 3 OBSTACLES:

1. _____
2. _____
3. _____

Projected Visualization - "Future Self Meditation"

LIST 3 "FUTURE SELF" SCENARIOS IN WHICH YOU ARE LIVING YOUR ENVISIONED LIFE.

1. _____
2. _____
3. _____

Expectations and Custom Goal Setting

☐ MY EXPECTATIONS ARE LINING UP WITH MY BELIEF SYSTEM.

LIST 3 "I AM" STATEMENTS:

1. _____
2. _____
3. _____

Reflection – "The Day's Lessons"

EVENT:_____

STUMBLE:_____

TOOL:_____

_____

_____

_____

_____

_____

H.A.P.P.I.N.E.S.S. Victories

LIST 3 EMOTIONAL VICTORIES YOU ACHIEVED TODAY:

1. _____

2. _____

3. _____

NUTRITION

☐ I AM HONORING MY BODY BY HONORING THE GUIDELINES OF MY NUTRITIONAL PLAN.

FITNESS

☐ I AM HONORING MY BODY BY HONORING MY SELECTED FITNESS PLAN.

SUPPORT

☐ I AM RECEIVING SUPPORT

☐ I AM GIVING SUPPORT

LIST 3 PEOPLE YOU RECEIVE SUPPORT FROM OR PROVIDE SUPPORT TO:

1. _____

2. _____

3. _____

MY SUPPORT TEAM IS:

☐ SAFE

☐ EMPATHETIC

☐ SOLUTION-FOCUSED

Born in Spirit Yet Grounded in Science

This is what I have ultimately come to understand regarding transformation: if the desire to transform is born in spirit, science will ground it by providing the tangible evidence of its realization.

Much of spirituality, faith, or religion will forever remain a mystery, and that is wonderful. Because through that wonderment we strengthen our faith in the unknown, and the mystical seems to draw us closer to the divine. I firmly believe God chose me to unravel the relationship between the God within us (Spirituality), our brain chemistry (Neuroscience), and the role redirecting our behavior (Behavioral Science) plays in lasting change. We are connected to God's divine power at a spiritual and cellular level; that is as ethereal, yet as human, as it gets.

This book was created to honor and share the gift of the emotional, physical, and spiritual liberation I received so many years ago. It was my goal in writing this book to demystify the spiritual without diminishing the importance of its mystery. The spirit is ethereal, and a beautiful gift from our Creator, but our Creator did not stop with spirit. He also provided us a human body that, through thought, will arrange itself to support our highest idea of ourselves. Our only job is to align with the goodness that is available to us through our thoughts and allow our bodies to do the rest. Our thoughts are that powerful!

Some of you will read this book and walk away with nothing more than interesting dinner conversation, while others will read it and walk away ready to embrace life on an entirely new level. The only difference between the two groups is belief and patience. Belief in the power you hold in your thoughts to align with the God force that lives within you — and the patience necessary to allow your physical, human body to catch up to your new joyful thinking.

The *Before the Fork* system is a continual loop. When you have worked through the Four Phases and experienced a 28-day cycle, take a deep breath and do it all over again. Allowing yourself to be the ultimate beginner, the rookie novice, the proficient practitioner, and the consummate expert is the greatest gift you can ever give yourself. An expert was once a beginner, so allow yourself to be a beginner over and over again. This cycle is the cycle of every timeless, unquestionable law of the universe. Use this knowledge with full confidence in its potential to change your life.

I would like to extend my deep love and appreciation for our time together and my great admiration for your desire to improve your life. My journey was, and will forever remain, an organic evolution of growth. I have spent over fourteen glorious years discovering, exploring, studying and applying tips, tools, and techniques to support my expansion. What was once a daily struggle is now a beautiful dance.

Each morning I have the singular goal of moving toward my vision while staying in alignment with my joy; I can think of no other use of my human potential more worthy than this. Please join me in striving to appreciate contrast while climbing the H.A.P.P.I.N.E.S.S. Ladder. I'll see you at the top; you'll recognize me... I'll be the one beaming with joy, yet so far from being complete!

With Great Love,
Robin

SECTION FOUR

Tips, Tools, and Techniques

Introduction to Tips, Tools, and Techniques

Welcome to the start of your own personal toolbox! Building a new YOU requires tools, and just like building a home, the right tool makes the job so much easier!

Your toolbox will cover several areas such as:
- State of Being Practices
- Social Environmental Practices
- In-Home Practices
- Miscellaneous Tips
- Identifying Saboteurs

State of Being Practices prepares your mind for transformation in several ways. They are designed to move you up the H.A.P.P.I.N.E.S.S. Ladder, help you with Process and Projected imagery (or Mental Rehearsal), assist you in releasing resistance and find deep appreciation, and even meditate to empower your Desired Self to stay in control.

Social Environmental Practices are special tips, tools, and techniques designed to help you in social settings. Whether learning to navigate dinner in a restaurant, a party with friends, a sporting event, or any other social engagement, developing tools will help you stay empowered and focused on your Desired Self.

In-Home Practices safeguard your home environment from the simplest, less obvious saboteurs. Learn how to prepare your refrigerator, put away your groceries, and even leave out snacks to better your odds of success.

Miscellaneous Tips utilize The Mindless Margin to create games that will motivate you to shave off a few calories here and there and pick up some calorie burn along the way. All through the simplest form of mindfulness. Specially designed games (250/250 and 1*2*3* Magic) will make this process fun.

Identifying Saboteurs is a simple handout that focuses on awareness and should be used alongside your journal pages to heighten your awareness of potentially compromising people, places, and things.

Before the Fork

Technique #1 – Descansos, Honor and Release (TR, Red, Yellow, Green)

THE MEANING OF DESCANSOS:
Descansos are markers of changes, turning points, even deaths (literal and figurative) in one's life. In Latin America they are the roadside shrines that mark the memory where an accident claimed a life. Metaphorically, we can also view them as crossroads, choice points, places where you choose one road and might have taken another.

The RELEASE OF RESISTANCE I experienced over 14 years ago was my first palpable Descansos. The feeling I had the moment I choose to honor and release my past is indescribable. It was so powerful I began a daily exercise of Descansos, I taught myself how to live in a 24-hour block of time, every night honoring and releasing and every morning appreciating and allowing.

How to do Descansos (3 minutes before sleep, 3 minutes after waking)
Bedtime:
Step one: Settle into your bed and begin by spending 15-20 seconds appreciating your environment, feel your soft pillow, linen spray, and crisp-cool sheets. (This is done to soften your resistance to the day in order to leave it behind).
Step two: Now that you are in a softer, more allowing place (Green Zone), acknowledge the moments of contrast you experienced through the day. Perhaps an argument, you blew your diet, you yelled at your child etc. Now, bless the contrast for allowing you the opportunity to expand. Mentally replace the behavior with a new desired behavior and allow that to become your new reality. Now, release.
Step three: Settle back into your bed, and repeat step one.

Awakening:
Step one: Ease into your day by choosing a soothing wake-up call (not a alarm clock).
Step two: Revisit the joy your bed brought you last night. Appreciate the softness of your pillow, your warm, buttery sheets and say a prayer of appreciation for the smallest of pleasures and begin your day.

This awakening process accomplishes two things:
1. It helps you begin your day in the Green Zone.
2. It reminds you that joy can be found in the smallest, most seemingly inconsequential places.

Robin Fun Fact: A Mindful Relaxation practice, such as Descansos, results in a deep physiological shift in the body, opposite of the stress response. This response can help ease many stress-related ailments, including depression, pain, and high blood pressure. For many people, sleep disorders are closely tied to stress.

Technique #2 – Visualization/Mental Rehearsal (TR, Red, Yellow, Green)
Visualization, or Mental Rehearsal involves mentally seeing and experiencing our "self" demonstrating or practicing a skill, habit or state of being of our own choosing.

Through Mental Rehearsal, we can employ the advanced faculties of our frontal lobe to make significant changes in our life. Throughout my reinvention process, I continue to use two types of mental rehearsal to assist in effecting change. They both require only 10 minutes per day.

Process Imagery: Process of imagining/seeing/feeling yourself overcoming difficult circumstances and using new skills in order to master any perceived challenge. Process Imagery is an important factor in developing expectations of success and self-confidence.

Examples of Process Imagery include:
- Driving past Starbucks and breaking the pattern of a daily 500 calorie Frappuccino
- Waking up an hour early to go for a walk/gym/meditate
- Healthier grocery shopping
- Performing well at an event
- Water over soda

Projected Imagery: A psychological technique that engages the frontal lobe incorporating all the senses (sight, hearing, taste, smell, touch) to paint a vivid and emotionally-driven connection to a desired future.

Areas of Projected Imagery include:
- Health
- Relationships
- Finance
- Spirituality
- Career

Technique #3 - Meditation (TR, Red, Yellow, Green)
Breath focus is a simple and powerful meditation technique.

Here is how to do it:
1. Sit still and stay put
   • Sit in a chair with your feet on the ground or with crossed legs on a cushion. Don't fidget, don't scratch itches, and don't move! Staying still is a huge part of why it helps willpower, as you learn not to follow every impulse your brain throws out.

2. Turn your attention to your breath
   • Close your eyes or focus on a single spot (like a blank wall). Begin to notice your breath. Silently in your mind say "inhale" as you breathe in and "exhale" as you breathe out. When your mind wanders (and it will) just bring it calmly back to the breath. Coming back to the breath again and again and again is what really stimulates the prefrontal cortex.

3. Notice how it feels to breathe, and notice how the mind wanders
   • After a few minutes, drop the inhale/exhale thoughts. Try just to focus on the sensation of breathing. You may sense the breath flowing in your mouth, maybe the rhythmic inflation/deflation of your chest, whatever. Your mind will still wander just calmly bring it back to the breath. If you need help refocusing, bring the inhale/ exhale thoughts back.

Start with 5 minutes a day, and once that is a habit bump it up to 15 a day. If that feels like a burden, drop it back to 5. A short practice every day is much better than a long practice every once in awhile. This technique is based on Kelly McGonigal's book, *Neuroscience of Change,* https://lifehacker.com/boost-your-willpower-with-this-meditation-technique-511060208

Robin Fun Fact: *Being bad at meditation is good for self-control. When you are bad at meditation you mind will wander A LOT. That skill translates directly into willpower. You notice you are off goal and then redirect, always refocusing back to the breath. This refocusing is almost like lifting a weight for your prefrontal cortex. So, don't be worried when you struggle. The struggle is what will improve your ability to focus and tap into newly developed willpower reserves.*

Technique #4 – Momentum Monologue (TR, Red, Yellow, Green)
This technique is when you are having a difficult time feeling better, or you want to savor and ENJOY even more the positive state of being created through green zone living.

The idea here is to allow a stream of wellbeing to flow through you, unobstructed. The worse you feel, the more you are resisting. This exercise will help you lower your resistance. You are literally moving your feelings up the H.A.P.P.I.N.E.S.S. Ladder. All you are going to do is write, say or ponder what you're appreciating in this moment.

1. If beginning from TR, Red, or Yellow Zones: Identify the emotion. Consider the two extreme ends (contrast). *Am I feeling powerless or powerful? Does it feel more like powerlessness or worry?* Continue until you can state accurately your feeling place.

2. Now find thoughts that help you find a little better feeling place about the situation. Talk out loud or write it out. Use the H.A.P.P.I.N.E.S.S. Ladder, and begin where you are. Fashion words that lead you into a slightly higher feeling place.

S Spectacular: joy, spiritual, knowledge, empowerment, freedom, love, appreciation, gratitude

S Sureness: positive, eagerness, happiness, enthusiasm, passion, belief

E Encouraged: hopeful, determined, inspired, confident, optimistic

N Neutral: content, calm, relaxed, unconcerned, unprejudiced

I Inattentive: bored, apathy, disinterested, complacent, indifferent

P Pessimism: frustration, sarcastic, discouragement, impatience, limited

P Problem focused: disappointment, doubt, worry

A Anger: resentment, hostile, rage, violence, jealousy, revenge

H Hatred: grief, depression, powerlessness, victim, shame

Robin Fun Fact: *Happy thoughts and positive thinking, in general, support brain growth, as well as the generation and reinforcement of new synapses, especially in your prefrontal cortex (PFC), which serves as the integration center of all of your brain-mind functions. In other words, your PFC not only regulates the signals that your neurons transmit to other brain parts and to your body, it allows you to think about and reflect upon what you are physically doing. In particular, the PFC allows you to control your emotional responses through connections to your deep limbic brain. It gives you the ability to focus on whatever you choose and to gain insight about your thinking processes. The PFC is the only part of your brain that can control your emotions and behaviors and help you focus on whatever goals you elect to pursue. It helps you grow as a human being, change what you wish to change, and live life the way you decide!*

Technique #4 – Momentum Monologue (TR, Red, Yellow, Green) - CONT'D

1. If beginning from Green Zone: Identify the green zone emotion (love, joy, appreciation, etc.).

2. Now find thoughts that help you continue the flow of emotions. Talk out loud or write it out. A stream of thoughts will effortlessly flow and you will produce chemicals that solidify this state of being, making it easier to pull yourself up from TR, Red and Yellow Zone emotions in the future.

I recommend falling in love with this technique while in the Green Zone, experiencing its power to perpetuate feelings of joy. Then, when you implement this practice from the TR, Red or Yellow Zone you will trust the technique's ability to soothe you into softer emotions.

Here is one of my Momentum Monologues from the Green Zone and one from the Red Zone.

Love Yourself First

and everything else falls into line. You really have to love yourself to get anything done in this world.

- Lucille Ball

Green Zone	TR, Red, Yellow Zone
I LOVE knowing that I'm okay,	I LOVE my work, but I am overwhelmed,
I LOVE being in this life,	I LOVE knowing I am doing what I was
I LOVE the excitement that each day brings,	born to do, but am I capable,
I LOVE listening to voices of my children,	I LOVE that I have dedicated 15 years to the study of my work,
I LOVE still getting butterflies when I look at my husband,	I LOVE that I allow contrast to be born from my experiences,
I LOVE I was raised with love and contrast by parents that adored me,	I LOVE that my work has helped people,
I LOVE my sisters and the comfort of those relationships,	I LOVE that my work was put in my heart from such a young age,
I LOVE the feeling of my great nephews little arms stretched around my neck,	I LOVE that contrast has helped light my path,
I LOVE doing what I enjoy,	**I LOVE that GOD provides all I need at the right time,**
I LOVE seeing the uniqueness in flower,	**I LOVE that He is perfectly capturing**
I LOVE knowing that I'm here for a reason,	**my passion to serve others through my curriculum,**
I LOVE flowing with the changes of the seasons,	I LOVE I have completed the first step in a series of life long dreams,
I LOVE feeling the joy in my heart,	I LOVE that everyday I find JOY in living and expanding,
I LOVE knowing that me and God are never apart,	I LOVE that I am never so overwhelmed I can't ZOOM OUT and gain my control again,
I LOVE feeling supported and I LOVE feeling LOVED,	I LOVE that my timing is always perfect,
I LOVE feeling peaceful in my body,	I LOVE that I am never finished,
I LOVE being open for something new,	I LOVE that I can't get it wrong,
I LOVE loving you,	I LOVE this opportunity to serve!
I LOVE letting LOVE be all that I see!	

The Mindless Margin

The Mindless Margin, is a term coined by Brian Wansink, Ph.D. in his book "Mindless Eating." The Mindless Margin is the margin or zone, in which we can either slightly overeat, or slightly under eat, without being aware of it.

According to Dr. Wansink, your body will not noticeably register (through hunger pains) a calorie deficit or calorie surplus of as much as 250 calories.

What does this mean for you?

It means that if you use my 250/250 or 1*2*3* Magic everyday, you can create a up to a 500 calorie deficit with very little added effort (250 nutritional calories saved, 250 physical calories burned).

What will this mean to your "Bottom" Line? Take a look...

250 calories saved through good choices (daily)
250 calories burned through mindful physical activity (daily)

500 calories deficit (daily)
x 7 days a week
=3,500 calories

A pound of body fat may contain anywhere between 3,436 and 3,752 calories, roughly estimated. Although weight loss is not a linear metabolic system, this approach is very effective in losing, maintaining and preventing weight loss and gain.

Bottom Line

Having FUN using 250/250 and 1*2*3* Magic and taking advantage of the body's natural Mindless Margin is a great way to approach weight loss!

Before the Fork

In Home Practices

What in-Home factors unknowingly influence our consumption? Being aware of hidden Saboteurs in our home environment is key to designing strategies to support our success.

What we buy, how we store it and, where we keep our snacks, all have an impact on our success.

Some examples:

- Big Box Quantity Snacks
- Pantry Party
- Super Size Me
- Big Man's Portion Platter
- Clean Plate Club
- Serving Platter on Table or Remain in the Kitchen

(Visit www.BeforetheFork.com to learn more.)

In-home Basics 101:

1. **Replace Your 12" Plate with a 10" Plate** - Serve yourself on smaller plates and taller glasses and use smaller utensils.
2. **Out of Sight Out of Mind** - Hide snacks away, or purge your home of unhealthy snacks.
3. **Make a Trade** - Swap your bagel for an English muffin, glass of whole milk for a glass of skim milk. Be creative and find a trade-off.
4. **Constantly Eat** - Never allow yourself to get too hungry. Constantly nosh on healthy snacks.
5. **Pack Ahead** - Portion out and pack snacks to take along with you (nuts un-shelled, fruit, healthy bars etc.).
6. **½ for ½** - If you are a soda drinker, cut your intake in half and replace the second half with water (If you typically drink 3 a day, only allow yourself 1 ½ cans of soda and replace the rest with water).
7. **Late Night Snacking** - Try taking a bath or shower, making a cup of tea, going for a walk or using the 10 minute pause rule to break the habit.
8. **Half Plate Healthy Plate** - Fill your plate ½ with vegetables/fruit, ¼ protein, ¼ grains
9. **Think 20% MORE or 20% LESS** - Think 20% LESS when you dish out your food or think 20% MORE for fruits and vegetables.
10. **Repackage Jumbo Boxes** - The bigger the package you pour from, the more you will eat: 20% to 30% more. Repackage your jumbo box into smaller Ziploc bags or Tupperware containers, and serve it up in smaller dishes.

11. **Keep it in the Kitchen** - Leave serving dishes in the kitchen and do not bring them to the table. This distance allows time for you to pause which is a very effective deterrent.
12. **Don't Deprive Yourself** - Deprivation will ultimately lead to a Feast or Famine mentality and we are only human. We must alter our habits without feeling deprived in order for the behavior to stick. Just stick to smaller portions.
13. **Sweet and Salty** - Create your own snack by mixing sweet and salty snacks together. This is more satisfying to your taste buds, just remember to portion out an appropriate serving size.

Before the Fork

What social environment factors unknowingly influence our consumption? Being aware of hidden Saboteurs in our social environment is key to designing strategies to support our success.

Rather than breaking this section into multiple categories of dining away from home, let's just lump social environment factors into one category called: AWAY.

Whenever we are away from our Home Base we become vulnerable to external influences. Some examples:

- Co-workers going to lunch
- Late night dinner invitations
- Happy Hour
- Sporting Events
- Holidays
- Parties

And the list goes on... Expect yourself to go through a few different emotions and scenarious when learning to navigate these treacherous waters.

1. Avoidance
2. Limited exposure
3. Trial and Error
4. Success

At first you may avoid the situations all together, turning down invitations to dinner, avoiding your co-workers or friends for lunch, working late as an excuse to skip out on Happy Hour, even declining a holiday event for fear it will completely de-rail you! Avoidance is a safe tactic, initially, but sooner or later, you have to engage in life again. There is a big difference in achieving a successful Lifestyle Transformation and living like a hermit!

Once you identify your Social Environment temptations and begin adding tools to your toolbox that may help you overcome the temptations, you may limit exposure and be very selective as to the events and circumstances you try out your new tools on! This is a safe thing to do.

Choose your occasions, and show up with a game plan.

Finally, SUCCESS!

Here are a few ideas to help you overcome Social Environment temptations:

Restaurants:

1. **Menu Preview** - Review the menu online prior to arriving at the restaurant and know exactly what you are going to order before the waiter or waitress arrives. Never open the menu.
2. **Program your choice into My Fitness Pal** prior to arriving at the restaurant.
3. **To-go Box FIRST** - Have the waitress deliver a to-go box with your meal. Before you even take a bite of your meal, divide it half and place one half in your to-go box.
4. **Eat Before You Eat** - Carry nuts in your car (organic, unsalted, blanched) and have 10 to 15 nuts on your way to the restaurant. This healthy fat and protein source will help to stabilize blood sugars and thwart off your hunger.
5. **Position yourself next to the slowest eater at the table.** We eat in a pack... so if you sit next to someone with a ravenous appetite, you are more likely to eat more.
6. **Position yourself away from the bread and chips**, or, if an option, ask them to skip the bread or chips and salsa all together. If skipping is not an option, sit at the very end of the table a long arm's reach from pre-meal goodies.
7. **Chew gum** during appetizers!
8. **Order double veggies, every time.** When asked what sides would you like, always request double veggies! Don't look over the menu just shout DOUBLE VEGGIES!
9. **Split a meal with anyone at the table!** Believe me someone at your table shares our weight loss goals, or they are on a thrifty budget and splitting a meal is the perfect solution.
10. **Never EVER ever drink your calories!** If you want to enjoy Happy Hour or a fruity-tootie drink, save it for your 20% Indulgence!

BONUS TIP: Carry snacks with you! Every where I go, I have an arsenal of snacks ready to combat my hunger. I am the go-to snack lady! Healthy, satiating, and delicious snacks are always just an arm's length away.

1*2*3* Magic Changes

We make over 200 food-related decisions every day. Long-term, sustainable and, most importantly, achievable healthy lifestyle reinvention is the result of overlapping these small, seemingly insignificant lifestyle choices on a daily basis. These "Power of THREE" changes will be subtle and barely detectable but will result in BIG LIFESTYLE CHANGES . You will have an opportunity to develop both food and non-food related changes.

Dr. Brian Wansink is an American professor in the fields of consumer behavior and nutritional science, he is also the author of **Mindless Eating**. I have incorporated many of his suggestions into my 80/20 philosophy and find great value in his pragmatic approach to lifestyle reinvention. Learn more about his work at mindlesseating.org.

Start using 1*2*3* Magic in your own life by incorporating (3) of these daily suggestions to help you move from mindless OVEREATING to mindless BETTER EATING:

1. **Replace your 12" plate with a 10" plate** – Serve yourself on smaller plates and taller glasses and use smaller utensils.
2. **Out of Sight Out of Mind** – Hide snacks away, or purge your home of unhealthy snacks.
3. **Make a Trade** – Swap your bagel for an English muffin, glass of whole milk for a glass of skim milk. Be creative and find a trade-off. See my 250/250 page for more of these!
4. **Split Your Lunch** - Split lunch with a friend .
5. **Half the Order** – When eating out, request a to-go box immediately and put half away.
6. **Constantly Eat** – Never allow yourself to get too hungry. Constantly nosh on healthy snacks.
7. **Pack Ahead** – Portion out and pack snacks to take along with you (nuts un-shelled, fruit, healthy bars etc.).
8. **½ for ½** – If you are a soda drinker, cut your intake in half and replace the second half with water (If you typically drink 3 a day, only allow yourself 1 ½ cans of soda and replace the rest with water).
9. **Plan PAUSE Points** – If you want an indulgent snack, wait 10 minutes and revisit the impulse. If you still want the treat, cut your portion in half.
10. **Pace Yourself** – If you are a fast eater find a pace-setter at your table; aim to eat equal to or slower than the slowest eater at the table.

11. **Late Night Snacking** – If you cave-in to late night snacking try taking a bath or shower, making a cup of tea, going for a walk or using the 10 minute pause rule to break the habit.

12. **Half Plate Healthy Plate** – Fill your plate ½ with vegetables/fruit, ¼ protein, ¼ grains.

13. **Think 20% MORE or 20% LESS** – Think 20% LESS when you dish out your food or think 20% MORE for fruits and vegetables.

14. **Repackage Jumbo Boxes** – The bigger the package you pour from, the more you will eat: 20% to 30% more. Repackage your jumbo box into smaller Ziploc bags or Tupperware containers, and serve it up in smaller dishes.

15. **Keep it in the Kitchen** – Leave serving dishes in the kitchen and do not bring them to the table. This distance allows time for you to pause which is a very effective deterrent.

16. **Don't Deprive Yourself** – Deprivation will ultimately lead to a Feast or Famine mentality and we are only human. We must alter our habits without feeling deprived in order for the behavior to stick. Just stick to smaller portions.

17. **Walk a Mile** – Going for a 1 mile walk (15 minute brisk paced) will burn 100 calories.

18. **Sweet and Salty** – Create your own snack by mixing sweet & salty snacks together. This is more satisfying to your taste buds, just remember to portion out an appropriate serving size.

19. **Journal** – Keep track of the foods you consume.

20. **Restaurant Rules** – (A typical restaurant meal can clock in at 1,200 calories)

    o Enjoy two of these, but not all three: an appetizer, a drink or a dessert. Share a dessert with a friend or ask for a take home box for the other half.

    o Ask the waiter not to bring the bread or chip basket to your table.

    o Start your meal off with sparkling water over a cocktail and save your cocktail to enjoy with the main course.

    o Alternate sparkling water with wine or add sparkling water to your wine for a wine spritzer.

    o If you must have bread choose the crunchy hard breads over soft doughy breads.

    o If you LOVE pasta, order it with protein. Remove ½ the pasta (place in the to-go that you have already asked your waiter to provide).

    o If you want to enjoy dessert, do not eat the bottom of the pie crust.

21. **Buffet Survival–**

   o Have a small healthy meal one or two hours before your party begins.
   o Wear snug clothes (you'll be less likely to over-eat).
   o Be Snobby... If you don't LOVE the food, don't eat it.
   o Direct your socializing away from the buffet table.
   o Check out the buffet before loading up your plate, wait 30 minutes and then revisit the buffet.
   o Skip the sauce laden dishes.
   o Chose the smallest plate available.
   o Fill half your plate with fresh whole foods (vegetables, fruit, nuts).

22. **In Addition to Watching Your Food, You Can...**

   1. Take the stairs (give up the elevator).
   2. If you have an hour for lunch, go for a 15 minute walk (100 calories = 1 mile).
   3. If watching TV do 10 pushups during commercial breaks.
   4. Walk to your mailbox instead of driving.
   5. Find 15 minutes and go for a power-walk (early morning, after-noon, after dinner, while dinner is cooking, at the mall).
   6. Park farther away from the department store (if the parking lot is safely lit).
   7. Before you begin shopping take two power-walking laps at the mall.
   8. If you have a Holiday Candy Jar on your desk, get rid of it.
   9. Choose an active house-chore (vacuuming, sweeping, moping, dusting, ironing). All of these activities are effective calorie burns when done with vigor and intention plus the house stays neat and tidy.

Saboteurs are everywhere and in the form of people, places and things. We all have triggers, whether they are people in our life that our relationship is centered around unhealthy eating habits (or smoking, drinking, gossip, etc.) or just simply a time of day, smell of cooking and more.

Again, being aware, engaging our Desired Self and allowing it to steer our behavior is a conscious choice. Highlighting these Saboteurs is the first step to containing them.

With the help of the previous handouts, keep on on-going list of Saboteurs. Then formulate a game plan to help contain and overcome their temptation.

Saboteur: Person, Place, or Thing

Strategy:_____

Keep a log of your saboteurs and strategy for containment.

Saboteur	Strategy

My 250/250 rule is designed to minimize overload in either exercise or caloric restriction. Being extreme in one area or the other is a sure fire way to sabotage success. Extreme exercise or extreme dieting can be detrimental to both your physical health as well as your psychological health.

By sharing the responsibility of Calories Burned (250) through exercise and Calories Saved (250) through modifying lifestyle choices we are adding an element of sustainability and creating an environment conducive to Lifestyle Reinvention. A 500 daily calorie deficit results in 1 lb. of weight loss a week.

Below, you will find a sampling of simple changes you could make in a week to lose 1 lb. without a huge effort! More tips can be found on my Facebook and Pinterest pages!

Calories Burned	Calories Saved	Total Calories
Running Up Stairs (25 min) **240**	Swap Mixed Nuts for Air Popped Popcorn **300+**	**540+**
Walk/Jog Combination (60 min) **295**	Swap Soda for Club Soda **300**	**595**
Chopping/Splitting Wood (30 min) **227**	Swap Large Cupcake for Mini Cupcake **500+**	**727**
Push Mowing Lawn (30 min) **205**	Swap Full Fat Ice Cream for Low Calorie **200+**	**405**
Dance, Dance, Dance (30 min) **200**	Swap Thick Crust Pizza for Thin Crust **500+**	**700**
Moderate Biking (40 min) **300**	Trade Chips for Veggies and Choose Whole Fruit Rather Than Juice **215**	**515**
Sweeping/Mopping Floors (30 min) **130**	Use a Salad Plate Rather Than a Dinner Plate **176**	**306**
	Total Weekly Calories for a 1lb.+ Weight Loss:	**3788!**

About the Author

Robin Shea has been entertaining and inspiring audiences with her passion and zest for life since 2002 through her television programs, speaking engagements, magazine articles, and lifestyle classes. She brings creative solutions to a variety of life's challenges such as raising positive children, creating a personal vision, the importance of the family dinner hour, the 80/20 Lifestyle solution to weight management, conquering your fears, and much more. Through her creative vision and dedication to helping individuals find their personal purpose in life, Robin empowers her audience with the courage to not only face, but embrace, the unknown.